BIOZONE

Cell Biology
& Biochemistry

The Biozone Writing Team

Tracey Greenwood

Lyn Shepherd

Richard Allan

Artwork by Daniel Butler

Published by:
Biozone International Ltd
109 Cambridge Road, Hamilton 2034, New Zealand

Printed by REPLIKA PRESS PVT LTD using paper
produced from renewable and waste materials

Distribution Offices:

United Kingdom & Europe	**Biozone Learning Media (UK) Ltd**, Scotland	
	Telephone:	+44 131-557-5060
	Fax:	+44 131-557-5030
	Email:	sales@biozone.co.uk
	Website:	www.biozone.co.uk
USA, Canada, South America, Africa	**Biozone International Ltd**, New Zealand	
	Telephone:	+64 7-856-8104
	Freefax:	1-800717-8751 (USA-Canada only)
	Fax:	+64 7-856-9243
	Email:	sales@biozone.co.nz
	Website:	www.biozone.co.nz
Asia & Australia	**Biozone Learning Media Australia**, Australia	
	Telephone:	+61 7-5575-4615
	Fax:	+61 7-5572-0161
	Email:	sales@biozone.com.au
	Website:	www.biozone.com.au

© 2006 **Biozone International Ltd**
ISBN: 1-877329-75-4
Second printing with minor corrections to pp. 14, 18-20, 28

Front cover photographs:
Diatoms. Image ©2005 JupiterImages Corporation www.clipart.com

Space filling model of a globular protein, rendered by MacPyMOL. ©2006 DeLano
Scientific LLC http://wwwpymol.org

NOTICE TO TEACHERS

Biology Modular Workbook Series

The Biozone *Biology Modular Workbook Series* has been developed to meet the demands of customers with the requirement for a modular resource which can be used in a flexible way. Like Biozone's popular Student Resource and Activity Manuals, these workbooks provide a collection of visually interesting and accessible activities, which cater for students with a wide range of abilities and background. The workbooks are divided into a series of chapters, each comprising an introductory section with detailed learning objectives and useful resources, and a series of write-on activities ranging from paper practicals and data handling exercises, to questions requiring short essay style answers. Material for these workbooks has been drawn from Biozone's popular, widely used manuals, but the workbooks have been structured with greater ease of use and flexibility in mind. During the development of this series, we have taken the opportunity to improve the design and content, while retaining the basic philosophy of a student-friendly resource which spans the gulf between textbook and study guide. With its unique, highly visual presentation, it is possible to engage and challenge students, increase their motivation and empower them to take control of their learning.

Cell Biology & Biochemistry

This title in the *Biology Modular Workbook Series* provides students with a set of comprehensive guidelines and highly visual worksheets through which to explore aspects of cell biology and biochemistry. *Cell Biology & Biochemistry* is the ideal companion for students of the life sciences, encompassing basic biochemistry, the structure and function of cells and their organelles, and an introduction to cell division and differentiation. This workbook comprises five chapters, each covering a different aspect of cell biology. These areas are explained through a series of one and two page activities, each of which explores a specific concept (e.g. diffusion or mitosis). Model answers (on CD-ROM) accompany each order free of charge. *Cell Biology & Biochemistry* is a student-centred resource. Students completing the activities, in concert with their other classroom and practical work, will consolidate existing knowledge and develop and practise skills that they will use throughout their course. This workbook may be used in the classroom or at home as a supplement to a standard textbook. Some activities are introductory in nature, while others may be used to consolidate and test concepts already covered by other means. Biozone has a commitment to produce a cost-effective, high quality resource, which acts as a student's companion throughout their biology study. Please do not photocopy from this workbook; we cannot afford to provide single copies of workbooks to schools and continue to develop, update, and improve the material they contain.

Acknowledgements and Photo Credits

Royalty free images, purchased by Biozone International Ltd, are used throughout this manual and have been obtained from the following sources: istockphotos (www.istockphoto.com) • Corel Corporation from various titles in their Professional Photos CD-ROM collection; ©Hemera Technologies Inc, 1997-2001; © 2005 JupiterImages Corporation www.clipart.com; PhotoDisc®, Inc. USA, www.photodisc.com. Biozone's authors also acknowledge the generosity of those who have kindly provided photographs for this edition (identified by way of coded credits): **BF**: Brian Finerran (University of Canterbury), **CDC**: Centers for Disease Control and Prevention, Atlanta, USA, **EII**: Education Interactive Imaging, **RCN**: Ralph Cocklin, **TG**: Tracey Greenwood, **WBS**: Warwick Silvester (University of Waikato), **WMU**: Waikato Microscope Unit.

Also in this series:

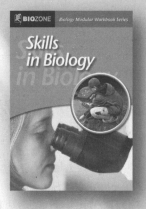

Skills in Biology

ISBN: 1-877329-71-1 (UK edition)

ISBN: 1-877329-72-X (International edition)

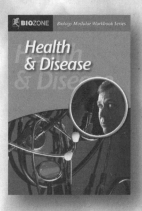

Health & Disease

ISBN: 1-877329-74-6

Microbiology & Biotechnology

ISBN: 1-877329-73-8

Contents

Activity is marked: ▪ to be done; ✓ when completed

How to Use this Workbook

Cell Biology & Biochemistry is designed to provide students with a resource that will make the acquisition of knowledge and skills in this area easier and more enjoyable. An understanding of cellular structure and function, and the structure and properties of important biological molecules is important in most biology curricula. Moreover, this subject is of high interest, with many applications in modern biotechnology based around understanding and exploiting the properties of cells and their constituents. This workbook is suitable for all students of the life sciences, and will reinforce and extend the ideas developed by teachers. It is **not a textbook**; its aim is to complement the texts written for your particular course. *Cell Biology & Biochemistry* provides the following resources in each chapter. You should refer back to them as you work through each set of worksheets.

Guidance Provided for Each Topic

Learning objectives:

These provide you with a map of the chapter content. Completing the learning objectives relevant to your course will help you to satisfy the knowledge requirements of your syllabus. Your teacher may decide to leave out points or add to this list.

Chapter content:

The upper panel of the header identifies the general content of the chapter. The lower panel provides a brief summary of the chapter content.

Key words:

Key words are displayed in **bold** type in the learning objectives and should be used to create a glossary as you study each topic. From your teacher's descriptions and your own reading, write your own definition for each word.

Note: Only the terms relevant to your selected learning objectives should be used to create your glossary. Free glossary worksheets are also available from our web site.

Use the check boxes to mark objectives to be completed.
Use a **dot** to be done (•).
Use a **tick** when completed (✓).

Supplementary texts:

References to supplementary texts suitable for use with this workbook are provided. Chapter references are provided as appropriate. The details of these are provided on page 7, together with other resources information.

Supplementary resources
Biozone's Presentation MEDIA are noted where appropriate.

Periodical articles:

Ideal for those seeking more depth or the latest research on a specific topic. Articles are sorted according to their suitability for student or teacher reference. Visit your school, public, or university library for these articles.

Internet addresses:

Access our database of links to more than **800** web sites (updated regularly) relevant to the topics covered. Go to Biozone's own web site: **www.thebiozone.com** and link directly to listed sites using the *BioLinks* button.

Activity Pages

The activities and exercises make up most of the content of this workbook. They are designed to reinforce the concepts you have learned about in the topic. Your teacher may use the activity pages to introduce a topic for the first time, or you may use them to revise ideas already covered. They are excellent for use in the classroom, and as homework exercises and revision. In most cases, the activities should not be attempted until you have carried out the necessary background reading from your textbook. As a self-check, model answers for each activity are provided on CD-ROM with each order of workbooks.

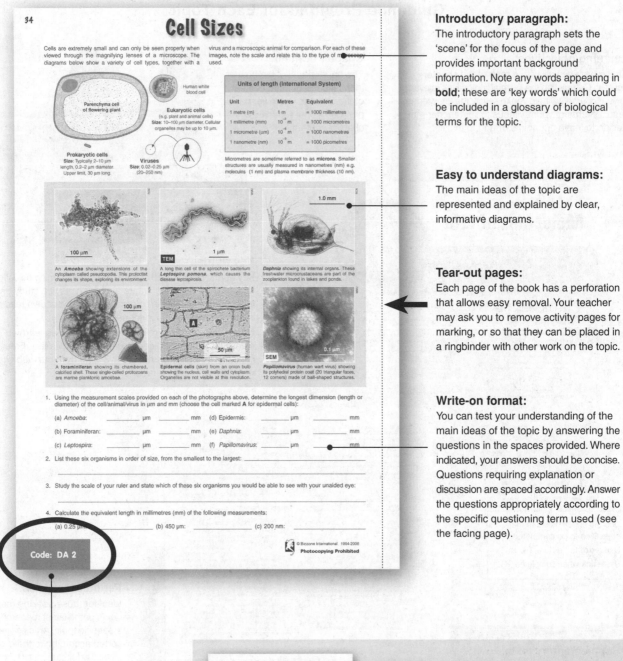

Introductory paragraph:
The introductory paragraph sets the 'scene' for the focus of the page and provides important background information. Note any words appearing in **bold**; these are 'key words' which could be included in a glossary of biological terms for the topic.

Easy to understand diagrams:
The main ideas of the topic are represented and explained by clear, informative diagrams.

Tear-out pages:
Each page of the book has a perforation that allows easy removal. Your teacher may ask you to remove activity pages for marking, or so that they can be placed in a ringbinder with other work on the topic.

Write-on format:
You can test your understanding of the main ideas of the topic by answering the questions in the spaces provided. Where indicated, your answers should be concise. Questions requiring explanation or discussion are spaced accordingly. Answer the questions appropriately according to the specific questioning term used (see the facing page).

Activity code:
Activities are coded to help you in identifying the type of activities and the skills they require. Most activities require some basic knowledge recall, but will usually build on this to include applying the knowledge to explain observations or predict outcomes. The least difficult questions generally occur early in the activity, with more challenging questions towards the end of the activity.

* Material to assist with the activity may be found on other pages of the workbook or in textbooks.

Activity Level

1 = Simple questions not requiring complex reasoning
2 = Some complex reasoning may be required
3 = More challenging, requiring integration of concepts

Type of Activity

D = Includes some data handling and/or interpretation
P = includes a paper practical
R = May require research outside the information on the page, depending on your knowledge base*
A = Includes application of knowledge to solve a problem
E = Extension material

Explanation of Terms

Questions come in a variety of forms. Whether you are studying for an exam or writing an essay, it is important to understand exactly what the question is asking. A question has two parts to it: one part of the question will provide you with information, the second part of the question will provide you with instructions as to how to answer the question. Following these instructions is most important. Often students in examinations know the material but fail to follow instructions and do not answer the question appropriately. Examiners often use certain key words to introduce questions. Look out for them and be clear as to what they mean. Below is a description of terms commonly used when asking questions in biology.

Commonly used Terms in Biology

The following terms are frequently used when asking questions in examinations and assessments. Students should have a clear understanding of each of the following terms and use this understanding to answer questions appropriately.

Account for: Provide a satisfactory explanation or reason for an observation.

Analyse: Interpret data to reach stated conclusions.

Annotate: Add **brief** notes to a diagram, drawing or graph.

Apply: Use an idea, equation, principle, theory, or law in a new situation.

Appreciate: To understand the meaning or relevance of a particular situation.

Calculate: Find an answer using mathematical methods. Show the working unless instructed not to.

Compare: Give an account of similarities and differences between two or more items, referring to both (or all) of them throughout. Comparisons can be given using a table. Comparisons generally ask for similarities more than differences (see contrast).

Construct: Represent or develop in graphical form.

Contrast: Show differences. Set in opposition.

Deduce: Reach a conclusion from information given.

Define: Give the precise meaning of a word or phrase as concisely as possible.

Derive: Manipulate a mathematical equation to give a new equation or result.

Describe: Give a detailed account, including all the relevant information.

Design: Produce a plan, object, simulation or model.

Determine: Find the only possible answer.

Discuss: Give an account including, where possible, a range of arguments, assessments of the relative importance of various factors, or comparison of alternative hypotheses.

Distinguish: Give the difference(s) between two or more different items.

Draw: Represent by means of pencil lines. Add labels unless told not to do so.

Estimate: Find an approximate value for an unknown quantity, based on the information provided and application of scientific knowledge.

Evaluate: Assess the implications and limitations.

Explain: Give a clear account including causes, reasons, or mechanisms.

Identify: Find an answer from a number of possibilities.

Illustrate: Give concrete examples. Explain clearly by using comparisons or examples.

Interpret: Comment upon, give examples, describe relationships. Describe, then evaluate.

List: Give a sequence of names or other brief answers with no elaboration. Each one should be clearly distinguishable from the others.

Measure: Find a value for a quantity.

Outline: Give a brief account or summary. Include essential information only.

Predict: Give an expected result.

Solve: Obtain an answer using algebraic and/or numerical methods.

State: Give a specific name, value, or other answer. No supporting argument or calculation is necessary.

Suggest: Propose a hypothesis or other possible explanation.

Summarise: Give a brief, condensed account. Include conclusions and avoid unnecessary details.

In Conclusion

Students should familiarise themselves with this list of terms and, where necessary throughout the course, they should refer back to them when answering questions. The list of terms mentioned above is not exhaustive and students should compare this list with past examination papers / essays etc. and add any new terms (and their meaning) to the list above. The aim is to become familiar with interpreting the question and answering it appropriately.

Using the Internet

The internet is a vast global network of computers connected by a system that allows information to be passed through telephone connections. When people talk about the internet they usually mean the **World Wide Web** (WWW). The WWW is a service that has made the internet so simple to use that virtually anyone can find their way around, exchange messages, search libraries and perform all manner of tasks. The internet is a powerful resource for locating information. Listed below are two journal articles worth reading. They contain useful information on what the internet is, how to get started, examples of useful web sites, and how to search the internet.

- **Click Here: Biology on the Internet** Biol. Sci. Rev., 10(2) November 1997, pp. 26-29.
- **An A-level biologists guide to The World Wide Web** Biol. Sci. Rev., 10(4) March 1998, pp. 26-29.

Using the Biozone Website: www.thebiozone.com

The **Back** and **Forward** buttons allow you to navigate between pages displayed on a www site

The current **internet address (URL)** for the web site is displayed here. You can type in a new address directly into this space.

Tool bar provides a row of buttons with shortcuts for some commonly performed tasks, such as printing a page or 'refreshing' the page (i.e. making the page load again).

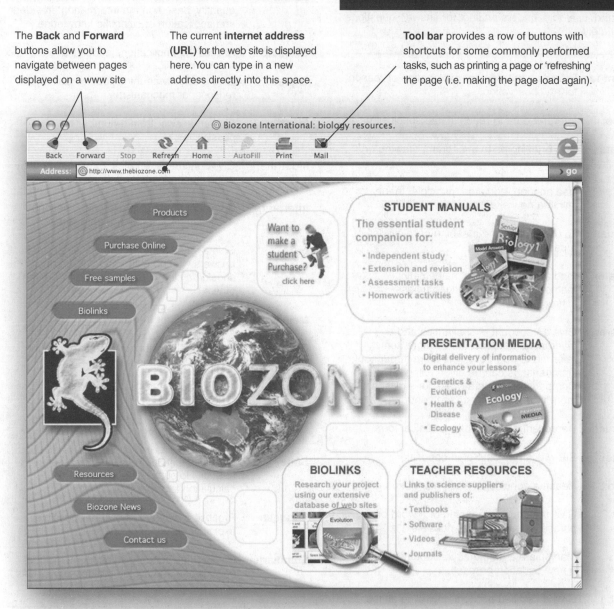

Searching the Net

The WWW addresses listed throughout the manual have been selected for their relevance to the topic in which they are listed. We believe they are good sites. Don't just rely on the sites that we have listed. Use the powerful 'search engines', which can scan the millions of sites for useful information. Here are some good ones to try:

Alta Vista:	**www.altavista.com**
Ask Jeeves:	**www.ask.com**
Excite:	**www.excite.com/search**
Google:	**www.google.com**
Go.com:	**www.go.com**
Lycos:	**www.lycos.com**
Metacrawler:	**www.metacrawler.com**
Yahoo:	**www.yahoo.com**

 © Biozone International 2006-2007

Biozone International provides a service on its web site that links to all internet sites listed in this workbook. Our web site also provides regular updates with new sites listed as they come to our notice and defunct sites deleted. Our **BIO LINKS** page, shown below, will take you to a database of regularly updated links to more than 800 other quality biology web sites.

The **Resource Hub**, accessed via the homepage or resources, provides links to the supporting resources referenced in the workbook. These resources include comprehensive and supplementary texts, biology dictionaries, computer software, videos, and science supplies. These can be used to enhance your learning experience.

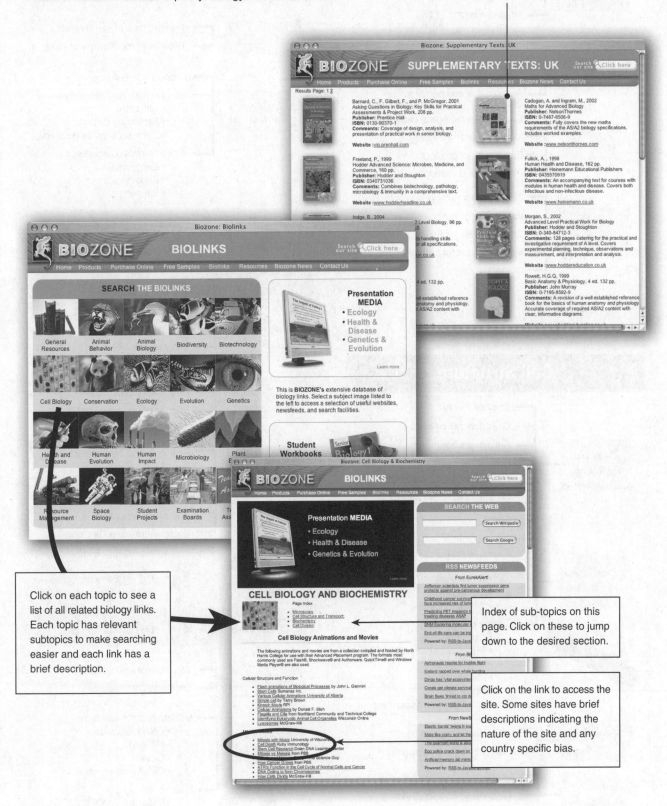

Click on each topic to see a list of all related biology links. Each topic has relevant subtopics to make searching easier and each link has a brief description.

Index of sub-topics on this page. Click on these to jump down to the desired section.

Click on the link to access the site. Some sites have brief descriptions indicating the nature of the site and any country specific bias.

Concept Map for Cell Biology

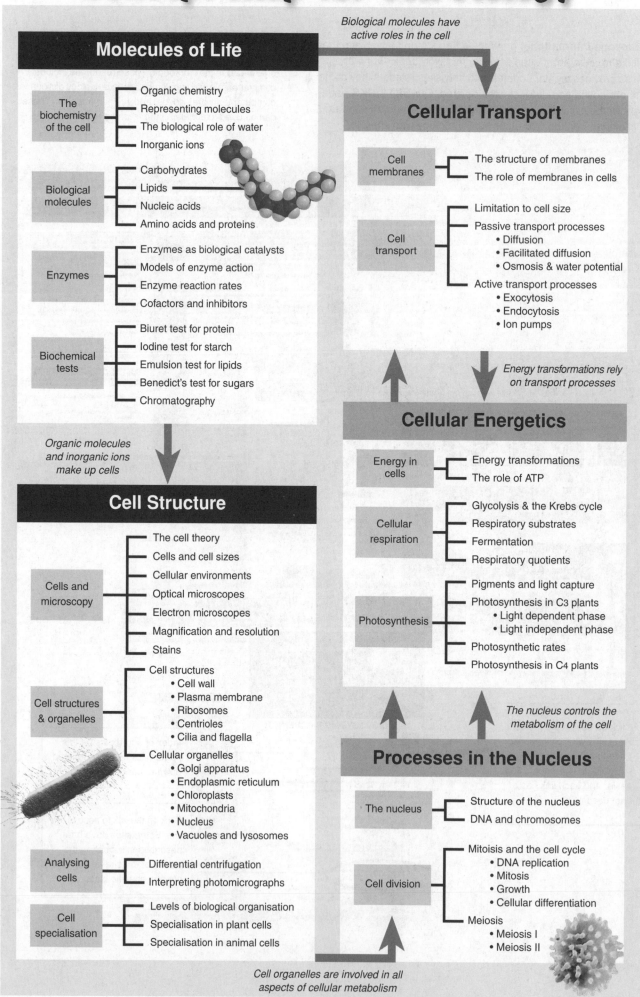

Biological molecules have active roles in the cell

Molecules of Life

The biochemistry of the cell
- Organic chemistry
- Representing molecules
- The biological role of water
- Inorganic ions

Biological molecules
- Carbohydrates
- Lipids
- Nucleic acids
- Amino acids and proteins

Enzymes
- Enzymes as biological catalysts
- Models of enzyme action
- Enzyme reaction rates
- Cofactors and inhibitors

Biochemical tests
- Biuret test for protein
- Iodine test for starch
- Emulsion test for lipids
- Benedict's test for sugars
- Chromatography

Cellular Transport

Cell membranes
- The structure of membranes
- The role of membranes in cells

Cell transport
- Limitation to cell size
- Passive transport processes
  - Diffusion
  - Facilitated diffusion
  - Osmosis & water potential
- Active transport processes
  - Exocytosis
  - Endocytosis
  - Ion pumps

Energy transformations rely on transport processes

Organic molecules and inorganic ions make up cells

Cell Structure

Cells and microscopy
- The cell theory
- Cells and cell sizes
- Cellular environments
- Optical microscopes
- Electron microscopes
- Magnification and resolution
- Stains

Cell structures & organelles
- Cell structures
  - Cell wall
  - Plasma membrane
  - Ribosomes
  - Centrioles
  - Cilia and flagella
- Cellular organelles
  - Golgi apparatus
  - Endoplasmic reticulum
  - Chloroplasts
  - Mitochondria
  - Nucleus
  - Vacuoles and lysosomes

Analysing cells
- Differential centrifugation
- Interpreting photomicrographs

Cell specialisation
- Levels of biological organisation
- Specialisation in plant cells
- Specialisation in animal cells

Cellular Energetics

Energy in cells
- Energy transformations
- The role of ATP

Cellular respiration
- Glycolysis & the Krebs cycle
- Respiratory substrates
- Fermentation
- Respiratory quotients

Photosynthesis
- Pigments and light capture
- Photosynthesis in C3 plants
  - Light dependent phase
  - Light independent phase
- Photosynthetic rates
- Photosynthesis in C4 plants

The nucleus controls the metabolism of the cell

Processes in the Nucleus

The nucleus
- Structure of the nucleus
- DNA and chromosomes

Cell division
- Mitoisis and the cell cycle
  - DNA replication
  - Mitosis
  - Growth
  - Cellular differentiation
- Meiosis
  - Meiosis I
  - Meiosis II

Cell organelles are involved in all aspects of cellular metabolism

Resources Information

Your set textbook should always be a starting point for information, but there are also many other resources available. A list of readily available resources is provided below. Access to the publishers of these resources can be made directly from Biozone's web site through our resources hub: **www.thebiozone.com/resource-hub.html**. Please note that our listing of any product in this workbook does not denote Biozone's endorsement of it.

Supplementary Texts

Adds, J., E. Larkcom & R. Miller, 2003. **Molecules and Cells**, revised ed. 112 pp. **ISBN**: 0-7487-7484-X
Includes coverage of biological molecules, with extra detail on nucleic acids and enzymes, cellular organisation, and cell division. Practical activities are provided for most chapters.

Adds, J., E. Larkcom, R. Miller, & R. Sutton, 1999. **Tools, Techniques and Assessment in Biology**, 160 pp. **ISBN**: 0-17-448273-6
A course guide covering basic lab protocols, microscopy, quantitative techniques in the lab and field, advanced DNA techniques and tissue culture, data handling and statistical tests, and exam preparation. Includes useful appendices.

Chenn, P., 1997. **Microorganisms and Biotechnology**, 176 pp. **ISBN**: 0-71957-509-5
Thorough coverage of the nature of microorganisms, their culture and growth, their various roles in biotechnology. It includes chapters on the genetic engineering of microbes and enzyme technology.

Clegg, C.J., 1998. **Mammals: Structure & Function**, 96 pp. **ISBN**: 0-7195-7551-6
A clearly written supplementary text covering most aspects of basic mammalian anatomy and physiology, as well as cells and tissues. Note: This text is now out of print from the publishers, but it is still available from amazon books.

Harwood, R. 2002. **Biochemistry**, 96 pp. **ISBN**: 0521797519
Methodical coverage of the structure and role of the main groups of biological molecules. Questions and exercises are provided and each chapter includes an introduction and summary.

Taylor, J., 2001. **Microorganisms and Biotechnology**, 192 pp. **Publisher**: NelsonThornes. Available in Australia through Thomson Learning **ISBN**: 0-17-448255-8
Comments: *Excellent coverage of the nature and biology of microorganisms, including prokaryotes, protists, and fungi.*

Tobin, A.J. and R.E Morel, 1997 **Asking About Cells**, 698 pp (paperback) **Publisher**: Thomson Brooks/Cole **ISBN**: 0-030-98018-6
Comments: *An introduction to cell biology, cellular processes and specialisation, DNA and gene expression, and inheritance. The focus is on presenting material through inquiry.*

Biology Dictionaries

Access to a good biology dictionary is useful when dealing with biological terms. Some of the titles available are listed below. Link to the relevant publisher via Biozone's resources hub or by typing: **www.thebiozone.com/resources/dictionaries-pg1.html**

Clamp, A. **AS/A-Level Biology. Essential Word Dictionary**, 2000, 161 pp. Philip Allan Updates. **ISBN**: 0-86003-372-4.
Carefully selected essential words for AS and A2. Concise definitions are supported by further explanation and illustrations where required.

Hale, W.G., J.P. Margham, & V.A. Saunders. **Collins: Dictionary of Biology** 3 ed. 2003, 672 pp. HarperCollins. **ISBN**: 0-00-714709-0.
Updated to take in the latest developments in biology from the Human Genome Project to advancements in cloning (new edition pending).

Henderson, I.F, W.D. Henderson, and E. Lawrence. **Henderson's Dictionary of Biological Terms**, 1999, 736 pp. Prentice Hall. **ISBN**: 0582414989
This edition has been updated, rewritten for clarity, and reorganised for ease of use. An essential reference and the dictionary of choice for many.

McGraw-Hill (ed). **McGraw-Hill Dictionary of Bioscience**, 2 ed., 2002, 662 pp. McGraw-Hill. **ISBN**: 0-07-141043-0
22 000 entries encompassing more than 20 areas of the life sciences. It includes synonyms, acronyms, abbreviations, and pronunciations for all terms.

Periodicals, Magazines, & Journals

Biological Sciences Review: *An informative quarterly publication for biology students.* Enquiries: **UK**: Philip Allan Publishers **Tel**: 01869 338652 **Fax**: 01869 338803 **E-mail**: sales@philipallan.co.uk **Australasia**: **Tel**: 08 8278 5916, **E-mail**: rjmorton@adelaide.on.net

New Scientist: *Widely available weekly magazine with research summaries and features.* Enquiries: Reed Business Information Ltd, 51 Wardour St. London WIV 4BN **Tel**: (UK and intl):+44 (0) 1444 475636 **E-mail**: ns.subs@qss-uk.com *or subscribe from their web site.*

Scientific American: *A monthly magazine containing specialist features. Articles range in level of reading difficulty and assumed knowledge.* Subscription enquiries: 415 Madison Ave. New York. NY10017-1111 **Tel**: (outside North America): 515-247-7631 **Tel**: (US& Canada): 800-333-1199

School Science Review: *A quarterly journal which includes articles, reviews, and news on current research and curriculum development. Free to Ordinary Members of the ASE or available on subscription.* Enquiries: **Tel**: 01707 28300 **Email**: info@ase.org.uk *or visit their web site.*

The American Biology Teacher: *The peer-reviewed journal of the NABT. Published nine times a year and containing information and activities relevant to biology teachers.* Contact: NABT, 12030 Sunrise Valley Drive, #110, Reston, VA 20191-3409 **Web**: www.nabt.org

© Biozone International 2006-2007

Molecules of Life

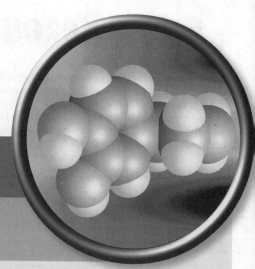

Understanding the biochemical nature of the cell and the role of enzymes in cells

Biological molecules (water, carbohydrates, lipids, proteins, and nucleic acids) and biochemical tests. Enzymes as biological catalysts.

Learning Objectives

☐ 1. Compile your own glossary from the **KEY WORDS** displayed in **bold type** in the learning objectives below.

Basic Organic Chemistry *(pages 10-11, 24)*

☐ 2. List the four most common elements found in living things. Provide examples of where these elements occur in cells. Explain what is meant by **organic chemistry** and explain its importance in biology.

☐ 3. Distinguish between ionic bonds and covalent bonds and understand the importance of **covalent bonds** in carbon-based compounds.

☐ 4. Distinguish between **monomers** and **polymers** and provide examples of each type. Explain clearly what is meant by a **macromolecule** and give examples.

☐ 5. Explain the basis of **chromatography** as a technique for separating and identifying biological molecules. Describe the calculation and use of **Rf values**.

Water and Inorganic Ions *(pages 11-12)*

☐ 6. Describe the structure of water, including reference to the polar nature of the water molecule, the nature of the bonding within the molecule, and the importance of **hydrogen bonding** *between* water molecules.

☐ 7. Identify the physical properties of water that are important in biological systems. Explain why water is termed the *universal solvent* and describe its various roles: *e.g. metabolic role, as a solvent, as a lubricant, and as a fluid in hydrostatic skeletons and cell turgor.*

☐ 8. Provide a definition of an **inorganic** (mineral) **ion**. With reference to specific examples, describe the role of inorganic ions in biological systems. Examples could include: Na^+, K^+, Mg^{2+}, Cl^-, NO_3^-, and PO_4^{3-}. Distinguish between **macronutrients** and **trace elements** and provide examples of each.

Carbohydrates *(pages 13-14, 24)*

☐ 9. Describe the basic composition and general formula of carbohydrates. Explain the main roles of carbohydrates in both plants and animals.

☐ 10. Describe what is meant by a **monosaccharide** and give its general formula. Provide examples of **triose**, **pentose**, and **hexose sugars** (including fructose and galactose). For each, identify its biological role.

☐ 11. Distinguish between **structural** and **optical isomers** in monosaccharides, explaining the basis for the isomerism in each case. Describe structural isomers of glucose (α and β **glucose**) and their biological significance.

☐ 12. Describe what is meant by a **disaccharide**. Explain how disaccharides are formed by a **condensation** reaction and broken apart by **hydrolysis**. Identify the **glycosidic bond** formed and broken in each case.

Give examples of disaccharides and their functions, and name the monosaccharides involved in each case.

☐ 13. Identify examples of **reducing** and **non-reducing sugars**, and describe the **Benedict's test** for distinguishing these. Explain the basis of the test and its result. Describe a test for a non-reducing sugar.

☐ 14. Explain what is meant by a **polysaccharide** and describe how polysaccharides are formed. Describe the molecular structure of the following examples of polysaccharides: *starch, glycogen, cellulose* and relate their structure to their function in biological systems.

☐ 15. Describe the I_2/KI (*iodine in potassium iodide solution*) **test** for starch. Explain its basis and result.

Lipids *(pages 15-16, 24)*

☐ 16. Describe the general properties of lipids. Recognise the diversity of lipids in biological systems and describe their functional roles. Consider: *phospholipids, waxes, steroids,* and *fats and oils*.

☐ 17. Describe the **emulsion test** for lipids. Explain the basis of the test and its result.

☐ 18. Recognise that most lipids are **triglycerides** (triacylglycerols). Describe how triglycerides are classified as *fats* or *oils* and explain the basis of the classification.

☐ 19. Using a diagram, describe the basic structure of a triglyceride. Explain their formation by **condensation** reactions between glycerol and three fatty acids. Identify the **ester bonds** that result from this. Distinguish between **saturated** and **unsaturated fatty acids** and relate this difference to the properties of the fat or oil that results.

☐ 20. Using a diagram, describe the basic structure of a **phospholipid** and explain how it differs from the structure of a triglyceride. Explain how the structure of phospholipids is important to their role in membranes.

Nucleic Acids *(pages 17-18)*

☐ 21. Name some examples of **nucleic acids** and describe their role in biological systems.

☐ 22. Describe the components of a (mono)**nucleotide**: a 5C sugar (**ribose** or **deoxyribose**), a nitrogenous base (**purine** or **pyrimidine**), and a phosphate. Identify the purines and pyrimidines that form nucleotides.

☐ 23. Understand the role of **condensation** reactions in joining the components of nucleotides and in the formation of dinucleotides and **polynucleotides** (nucleic acids).

☐ 24. Describe the Watson-Crick **double-helix** model of DNA structure. Include reference to the **base pairing rule**, the **antiparallel strands**, and the role of **hydrogen bonding** between **purines** and **pyrimidines**. Contrast the structure and function of **DNA** and **RNA**.

Amino Acids and Proteins *(pages 19-24)*

☐ 25. Draw or describe the general structure and formula of an **amino acid**. Explain the basis for the different properties of amino acids.

☐ 26. Recognise that, of over 170 amino acids, only 20 are commonly found in proteins. Distinguish between **essential** and **non-essential amino acids**.

☐ 27. Recognise the property of **optical isomerism** in amino acids and explain its basis. Distinguish L- and D- forms and identify which isomer is active in biological systems.

☐ 28. Using a diagram, describe how amino acids are joined together in a **condensation reaction** to form **dipeptides** and **polypeptides**. Describe the nature of **peptide bonds** that result. Describe how polypeptides are broken down by **hydrolysis**.

☐ 29. Describe the **biuret test** for proteins. Explain the basis of the test and its result.

☐ 30. Identify where (in the cell) proteins are made and recognise the ways in which they can be modified after production. Distinguish between the **primary structure** of a protein and its **secondary structure**.

☐ 31. Recognise the two main types of secondary structure found in proteins: *alpha-helix* and *beta-pleated sheet*.

☐ 32. Explain what is meant by the **tertiary structure** of a protein and explain how it arises. Describe the relationship between the tertiary structure of a **globular protein** and its biological function.

☐ 33. With reference to examples (e.g. collagen and insulin or haemoglobin), distinguish between **globular** and **fibrous proteins**. Consider the structure, properties, and biological functions of the protein.

☐ 34. With reference to specific examples (e.g. collagen, insulin, haemoglobin), describe the role of different types of bonds in proteins: *hydrogen bonds*, *ionic bonds*, *disulfide bonds*, *hydrophobic interactions*.

☐ 35. Explain what is meant by protein **denaturation** and explain why it destroys the activity of proteins. Describe how different agents denature proteins.

☐ 36. Explain what is meant by the **quaternary structure** of a protein. In a named example (e.g. *haemoglobin, a globular protein*) describe how the quaternary structure arises and relate it to the protein's function.

☐ 37. Recognise the ways in which proteins can be classified:
- By their structure (e.g. *globular* or *fibrous*)
- By their functional role: *structural, protective (role in immunity), as enzymes, as hormones, as respiratory pigments, in transport, contractile, in storage*.

Enzymes *(pages 25-28)*

☐ 38. Define: **enzyme**, **catalyst**, **active site**, and **substrate**. Describe the general properties of enzymes and explain their role in regulating cell metabolism.

☐ 39. Explain the mechanism by which enzymes work as catalysts to bring about reactions in cells. Define: **enzyme-substrate complex**, **activation energy**.

☐ 40. Contrast the **induced fit** and the **lock and key** models of enzyme function, clearly explaining how they differ.

☐ 41. Describe ways in which the time course of an enzyme-catalysed reaction can be followed: by measuring the rate of product formation (*e.g. catalase*) or by measuring the rate of substrate use (*e.g. amylase*).

☐ 42. Distinguish between **coenzymes** and **cofactors**. Explain how cofactors enable an enzyme to work.

☐ 43. Distinguish **reversible** from **irreversible** inhibition. Describe the effects of **competitive** and **non-competitive inhibitors** on enzyme activity.

☐ 44. Describe the effect of the following factors on enzyme activity: *substrate concentration, enzyme concentration, pH, temperature*. Identify the **optimum conditions** for some named enzymes. Recognise that enzymes (being proteins) can be **denatured**.

Molecules of Life

See page 7 for additional details of these texts:

■ Adds, J. *et al.*, 2003. **Molecules and Cells**, (NelsonThornes), chpt. 1-3.

■ Adds, J., E. Larkcom, R. Miller, & R. Sutton, 1999. **Tools, Techniques and Assessment in Biology**, (NelsonThornes), as required.

■ Harwood, R., 2002. **Biochemistry**, (Cambridge University Press), entire text.

■ Tobin, A.J. and Morel, R.E., 1997. **Asking About Cells**, (Thomson Brooks/Cole), as required.

See page 7 for details of publishers of periodicals:

■ **Biochemistry** Biol. Sci. Rev., 20(2) Nov. 2007, pp. 21-24. *An outline of what constitutes biochemistry and its role as a essential discipline within science.*

Presentation MEDIA to support this topic:

CELL BIO & BIOCHEM
• **Molecules of Life**

Cell Biology & Biochemistry

■ **Stuck with Structures?** Biol. Sci. Rev., 19(1) Sept. 2006, pp. 10-11. *A guide to interpreting the structural formulae of common organic compounds.*

■ **Designer Starches** Biol. Sci. Rev., 19(3) Feb. 2007, pp. 18-20. *The composition of starch, and an excellent account of its properties and functions.*

■ **Of Hydrogen Bondage** Biol. Sci. Rev., 10(1) Sept. 1997, pp. 36-38. *The critical role of hydrogen bonding in biological molecules and water.*

■ **Why Life Chose Carbon** Biol. Sci. Rev., 10(2) November 1997, pp. 15-17. *The structure of the carbon atom and its role in biological chemistry.*

■ **Glucose and Glucose-Containing Carbohydrates** Biol. Sci. Rev., 19(1) Sept. 2006, pp. 12-15. *The structure and biological functions of glucose and glucose containing polymers.*

■ **D-Glucose: A Shapely, Stable Molecule** Biol. Sci. Rev., 16(2) Nov. 2003, pp. 15-20. *Properties of glucose: a small, six carbon sugar.*

■ **Foetal Haemoglobin** Biol. Sci. Rev., 16(1) Sept. 2003, pp. 15-17. *The complex quaternary structure of haemoglobin molecules.*

■ **Making Proteins Work (I)** Biol. Sci. Rev., 15(1) Sept. 2002, pp. 22-25. *A synopsis of how a globular and a fibrous protein each become functional.*

■ **Making Proteins Work (II)** Biol. Sci. Rev., 15(2) Nov. 2002, pp. 24-27. *How carbohydrates are added to proteins to make them functional.*

■ **Enzymes** Biol. Sci. Rev., 15(1) Sept. 2002, pp. 2-5. *Enzymes as catalysts: how they work, models of enzyme function, and cofactors and inhibitors.*

■ **Smart Proteins** New Scientist, 17 March 2001 (Inside Science). *The structure and role of proteins.*

■ **Enzymes: Fast and Flexible** Biol. Sci. Rev., 19(1) Sept. 2006, pp. 2-5. *An excellent account of enzyme function, including a clear diagrammatic treatment of the induced fit theory.*

■ **Exploring Proteins** Biol. Sci. Rev., 16(4) April 2004, pp. 32-36. *Understanding how proteins function as complexes within the cell. Chromatographic techniques are also described.*

■ **Universal Body Builder** New Scientist, 23 May 1998 (Inside Science). *The structure and role of collagen, the most common protein in animals.*

See pages 4-5 for details of how to access **Bio Links** from our web site: **www.thebiozone.com** From Bio Links, access sites under the topics:

GENERAL BIOLOGY ONLINE RESOURCES > **Online Textbooks and Lecture Notes** • An on-line biology book • Learn.co.uk • S-cool!: A level biology revision guide • The biology project • The open door web site • Welcome to the biology web ... *and others* > **General online biology resources**: • Access Excellence • Biology I: Interactive animations • Ken's bio-web resources ... *and others* > **Glossaries**: • Cellular biology: Glossary of terms • Kimball's biology glossary

BIOTECHNOLOGY > **Applications in Biotechnology** > **Industrial Biotechnology**: • About industrial enzymes • Chapter 19: industrial microbiology • Discover enzymes ... *and others* **CELL BIOLOGY AND BIOCHEMISTRY**: • Cell structure and function web links ... *and others* > **Biochemistry and Metabolic Pathways**: • Enzymes • Energy, enzymes, and catalysis problem set • Energy and enzymes • Metabolism and Biochemistry • Reactiona and enzymes • The Biology Project: Biochemistry ... *and others*

The Biochemical Nature of the Cell

The molecules that make up living things can be grouped into five classes: water, carbohydrates, lipids, proteins, and nucleic acids. Water is the main component of organisms and provides an environment in which metabolic reactions can occur. Water molecules attract each other, forming large numbers of hydrogen bonds. It is this feature that gives water many of its unique properties, including its low viscosity and its chemical behaviour as a **universal solvent**. Apart from water, most other substances in cells are compounds of carbon, hydrogen, oxygen, and nitrogen. The combination of carbon atoms with the atoms of other elements provides a huge variety of molecular structures. These are described on the following pages.

Important Properties of Water

Water is a liquid at room temperature and many substances dissolve in it. It is a medium inside cells and for aquatic life.

A lot of energy is required before water will change state so aquatic environments are thermally stable and sweating and transpiration cause rapid cooling.

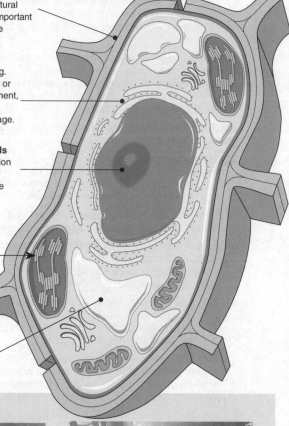

Carbohydrates form the structural components of cells, they are important in energy storage, and they are involved in cellular recognition.

Proteins may be structural (e.g. collagen), catalytic (enzymes), or they may be involved in movement, message signalling, internal defence and transport, or storage.

Nucleotides and nucleic acids Nucleic acids encode information for the construction and functioning of an organism. The nucleotide, ATP, is the energy currency of the cell.

Lipids provide insulation and a concentrated source of energy. Phospholipids are a major component of cellular membranes.

Water is a major component of cells: many substances dissolve in it, metabolic reactions occur in it, and it provides support and turgor.

Ice is less dense than water. Consequently ice floats, insulating the underlying water and providing valuable habitat.

Water has a high surface tension and low viscosity. It forms droplets on surfaces and can flow freely through narrow vessels.

Water is colourless, with a high transmission of visible light, so light penetrates tissue and aquatic environments.

1. Explain the biological significance of each of the following physical properties of water:

   (a) Low viscosity: _____

   (b) Colourless and transparent: _____

   (c) Universal solvent: _____

   (d) Ice is less dense than water: _____

2. Identify the biologically important role of each of the following molecules:

   (a) Lipids: _____

   (b) Carbohydrates: _____

   (c) Proteins: _____

   (d) Nucleic acids: _____

Biological Molecules

An understanding of the structure and function of the five classes of molecules that make up living things is necessary to many branches of biology, especially biochemistry, physiology, and molecular genetics. The diagram below illustrates some of the common ways in which biological molecules are portrayed. Note that the **molecular formula** expresses the number of atoms in a molecule, but does not convey its structure; this is indicated by the **structural formula**. Different types of models use different symbolism to represent the same information visually. The role of water in biological systems is described over the page.

Portraying Biological Molecules

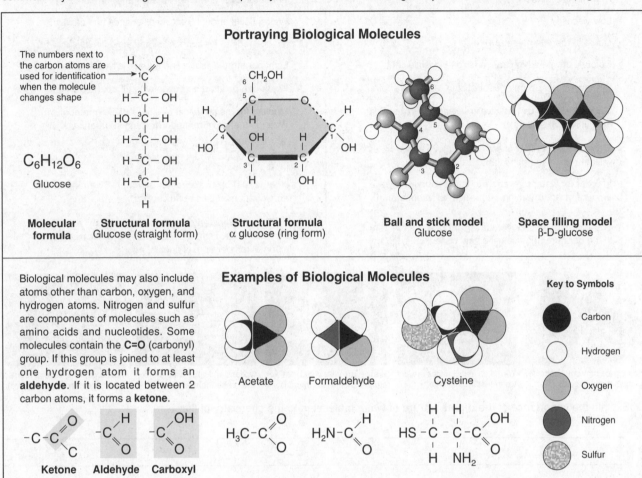

| Molecular formula | Structural formula Glucose (straight form) | Structural formula α glucose (ring form) | Ball and stick model Glucose | Space filling model β-D-glucose |

Biological molecules may also include atoms other than carbon, oxygen, and hydrogen atoms. Nitrogen and sulfur are components of molecules such as amino acids and nucleotides. Some molecules contain the **C=O** (carbonyl) group. If this group is joined to at least one hydrogen atom it forms an **aldehyde**. If it is located between 2 carbon atoms, it forms a **ketone**.

Examples of Biological Molecules

Key to Symbols: Carbon, Hydrogen, Oxygen, Nitrogen, Sulfur

Acetate, Formaldehyde, Cysteine

Ketone, Aldehyde, Carboxyl

Water and Inorganic Ions

Water provides an environment in which metabolic reactions can happen. Water takes part in, and is a common product of, many reactions. The most important feature of the chemical behaviour of water is its **dipole** nature. It has a small positive charge on each of the two hydrogens and a small negative charge on the oxygen.

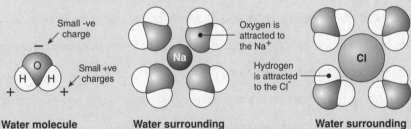

Water molecule Formula: H_2O — Water surrounding a positive ion (Na^+) — Water surrounding a negative ion (Cl^-)

Inorganic ions are important for the structure and metabolism of all living organisms. An ion is simply an atom (or group of atoms) that has gained or lost one or more electrons. Many of these ions are soluble in water. Some of the inorganic ions required by organisms and their biological roles are listed in the table on the right.

Ion	Name	Biological role
Ca^{2+}	Calcium	Component of bones and teeth
Mg^{2+}	Magnesium	Component of chlorophyll
Fe^{2+}	Iron (II)	Component of haemoglobin
NO_3^-	Nitrate	Component of amino acids
PO_4^{3-}	Phosphate	Component of nucleotides
Na^+	Sodium	Involved in the transmission of nerve impulses
K^+	Potassium	Involved in controlling plant water balance
Cl^-	Chloride	Involved in the removal of water from urine

1. On the diagram above, showing a positive and a negative ion surrounded by water molecules, draw the positive and negative charges on the water molecules (as shown in the example provided in the same panel).

Molecules of Life

Code: A 1

Biologically Important Properties of Water

Property of water	Significance for life
Ice is less dense than water.	Ice floats and also insulates the underlying water.
High surface tension.	Water forms droplets on surfaces and runs off.
Low viscosity.	Water flows through very small spaces and capillaries.
Liquid at room temperature.	Liquid medium for aquatic life and inside cells.
Colourless with a high transmission of visible light.	Light penetrates tissue and aquatic environments.
Strong cohesive properties and high tensile strength.	Water can be lifted and does not pull apart easily.
Many substances can dissolve in water (i.e. it is classified as a universal solvent).	Medium for the chemical reactions of life (metabolism). Water is the main transport medium in organisms.
Significant amounts of energy are required before water will change state (high latent heat of fusion)	Contents of cells are unlikely to freeze.
In order for water to evaporate it must absorb a large amount of energy (high latent heat of vaporisation).	Heat is lost by evaporation of water. Sweating and transpiration causes rapid cooling.
Water can absorb a lot of energy for only a small rise in temperature (high specific heat capacity).	Aquatic environments are thermally stable. Organisms have stable internal temperatures when the external temperature is fluctuating.

Floating ice provides habitat for animals such as seals.

Waxes on leaf surfaces prevent water loss from plants.

Water provides habitat for aquatic plants and animals.

Oceans and large water bodies tend to be thermally stable.

Most organisms require regular water intake (active or passive).

2. Explain the importance of the **dipole nature** of water molecules to the chemistry of life:

_____

_____

3. Identify the three main elements comprising the structure of organic molecules: _____

_____

4. Name two other elements that are also frequently part of organic molecules: _____

5. State how many covalent bonds a carbon atom can form with neighbouring atoms: _____

6. Classify formaldehyde according to the position of the C=O group: _____

7. For (a)-(e), state the property of water that is significant, and give one example of that property's biological importance:

(a) Property important in clarity of seawater: _____

Biological importance: _____

(b) Property important in water travelling up the xylem tissue in plants: _____

Biological importance: _____

(c) Property important in transport of glucose around the body: _____

Biological importance: _____

(d) Property important in the relatively stable temperature of water bodies: _____

Biological importance: _____

(e) Property important in the cooling effect of evaporation: _____

Biological importance: _____

Carbohydrates

Carbohydrates are a family of organic molecules made up of carbon, hydrogen, and oxygen atoms with the general formula $(CH_2O)_x$. The most common arrangements found in sugars are hexose (6 sided) or pentose (5 sided) rings. Simple sugars, or monosaccharides, may join together to form compound sugars (disaccharides and polysaccharides), releasing water in the process (**condensation**). Compound sugars can be broken down into their constituent monosaccharides by the opposite reaction (**hydrolysis**). Sugars play a central role in cells, providing energy and, in some cells, contributing to support. They are the major component of most plants (60-90% of the dry weight) and are used by humans as a cheap food source, and a source of fuel, housing, and clothing. In all carbohydrates, the structure is closely related to their functional properties (below).

Monosaccharides

Monosaccharides are used as a primary energy source for fuelling cell metabolism. They are **single-sugar** molecules and include glucose (grape sugar and blood sugar) and fructose (honey and fruit juices). The commonly occurring monosaccharides contain between three and seven carbon atoms in their carbon chains and, of these, the 6C hexose sugars occur most frequently. All monosaccharides are classified as **reducing** sugars (i.e. they can participate in reduction reactions).

Single sugars (monosaccharides)

Triose

C
|
C
|
C

e.g. glyceraldehyde

Pentose

e.g. ribose, deoxyribose

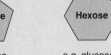

Hexose

e.g. glucose, fructose, galactose

Disaccharides

Disaccharides are **double-sugar** molecules and are used as energy sources and as building blocks for larger molecules. The type of disaccharide formed depends on the monomers involved and whether they are in their α- or β- form. Only a few disaccharides (e.g. lactose) are classified as reducing sugars.

Sucrose = α-glucose + β-fructose (simple sugar found in plant sap)
Maltose = α-glucose + α-glucose (a product of starch hydrolysis)
Lactose = β-glucose + β-galactose (milk sugar)
Cellobiose = β-glucose + β-glucose (from cellulose hydrolysis)

Double sugars (disaccharides)

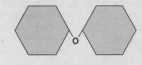

Examples sucrose, lactose, maltose, cellobiose

Polysaccharides

Cellulose: Cellulose is a structural material in plants and is made up of unbranched chains of β-**glucose** molecules held together by **1, 4 glycosidic links**. As many as 10 000 glucose molecules may be linked together to form a straight chain. Parallel chains become cross-linked with hydrogen bonds and form bundles of 60-70 molecules called microfibrils. Cellulose microfibrils are very strong and are a major component of the structural components of plants, such as the cell wall (photo, right).

Starch: Starch is also a polymer of glucose, but it is made up of long chains of α-**glucose** molecules linked together. It contains a mixture of 25-30% **amylose** (unbranched chains linked by α-1, 4 glycosidic bonds) and 70-75% **amylopectin** (branched chains with α-1, 6 glycosidic bonds every 24-30 glucose units). Starch is an energy storage molecule in plants and is found concentrated in insoluble **starch granules** within plant cells (see photo, right). Starch can be easily hydrolysed by enzymes to soluble sugars when required.

Glycogen: Glycogen, like starch, is a branched polysaccharide. It is chemically similar to amylopectin, being composed of α-**glucose** molecules, but there are more α-1,6 glycosidic links mixed with α-1,4 links. This makes it more highly branched and water-soluble than starch. Glycogen is a storage compound in animal tissues and is found mainly in **liver** and **muscle** cells (photo, right). It is readily hydrolysed by enzymes to form glucose.

Chitin: Chitin is a tough modified polysaccharide made up of chains of β-**glucose** molecules. It is chemically similar to cellulose but each glucose has an amine group (–NH2) attached. After cellulose, chitin is the second most abundant carbohydrate. It is found in the cell walls of fungi and is the main component of the **exoskeleton** of insects (right) and other arthropods.

BF
Cellulose

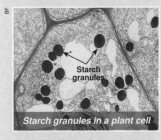

BF
Starch granules
Starch granules in a plant cell

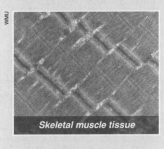

WMU
Skeletal muscle tissue

Chitinous insect exoskeleton

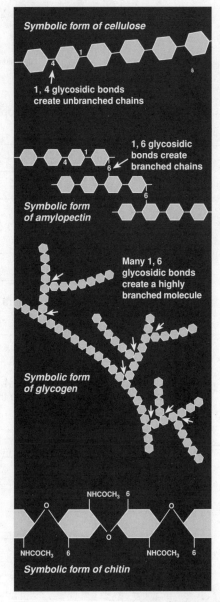

Symbolic form of cellulose

1, 4 glycosidic bonds create unbranched chains

1, 6 glycosidic bonds create branched chains

Symbolic form of amylopectin

Many 1, 6 glycosidic bonds create a highly branched molecule

Symbolic form of glycogen

NHCOCH₃ 6

NHCOCH₃ 6

NHCOCH₃ 6

Symbolic form of chitin

Molecules of Life

Code: A 2

Isomerism

Compounds with the same chemical formula (same types and numbers of atoms) may differ in the arrangement of their atoms. Such variations in the arrangement of atoms in molecules are called **isomers**. In **structural isomers** (such as fructose and glucose, and the α and β glucose, right), the atoms are linked in different sequences. **Optical isomers** are identical in every way but are mirror images of each other.

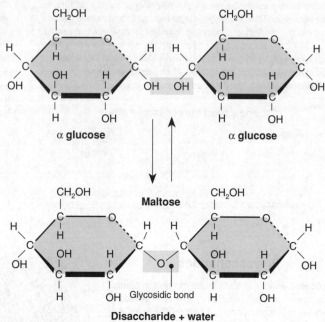

α glucose   β glucose

Condensation and Hydrolysis Reactions

Monosaccharides can combine to form compound sugars in what is called a **condensation** reaction. Compound sugars can be broken down by **hydrolysis** to simple monosaccharides.

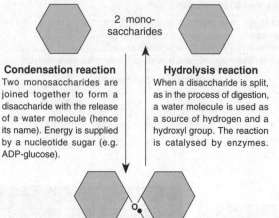

2 mono-saccharides

Condensation reaction
Two monosaccharides are joined together to form a disaccharide with the release of a water molecule (hence its name). Energy is supplied by a nucleotide sugar (e.g. ADP-glucose).

Hydrolysis reaction
When a disaccharide is split, as in the process of digestion, a water molecule is used as a source of hydrogen and a hydroxyl group. The reaction is catalysed by enzymes.

+
H_2O Glycosidic bond

Disaccharide + water

α glucose   α glucose

Maltose

Glycosidic bond

Disaccharide + water

1. Distinguish between structural and optical isomers in carbohydrates, describing examples of each:

_____

_____

_____

2. Explain how the isomeric structure of a carbohydrate may affect its chemical behaviour: _____

_____

_____

3. Explain briefly how compound sugars are formed and broken down: _____

_____

_____

4. Discuss the structural differences between the polysaccharides cellulose, starch, and glycogen, explaining how the differences in structure contribute to the functional properties of the molecule:

_____

_____

_____

_____

_____

_____

_____

Lipids

Lipids are a group of organic compounds with an oily, greasy, or waxy consistency. They are relatively insoluble in water and tend to be water-repelling (e.g. cuticle on leaf surfaces). Lipids are important biological fuels, some are hormones, and some serve as structural components in plasma membranes. Proteins and carbohydrates may be converted into fats by enzymes and stored within cells of adipose tissue. During times of plenty, this store is increased, to be used during times of food shortage.

Neutral Fats and Oils

The most abundant lipids in living things are **neutral fats**. They make up the fats and oils found in plants and animals. Fats are an economical way to store fuel reserves, since they yield more than twice as much energy as the same quantity of carbohydrate. Neutral fats are composed of a glycerol molecule attached to one (monoglyceride), two (diglyceride) or three (triglyceride) fatty acids. The fatty acid chains may be saturated or unsaturated (see below). **Waxes** are similar in structure to fats and oils, but they are formed with a complex alcohol instead of glycerol.

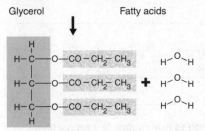

Triglyceride: an example of a neutral fat

Condensation

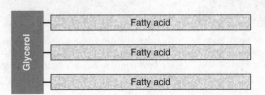

Glycerol   Fatty acids

Triglycerides form when glycerol bonds with three fatty acids. Glycerol is an alcohol containing three carbons. Each of these carbons is bonded to a hydroxyl (-OH) group.

When glycerol bonds with the fatty acid, an **ester bond** is formed and water is released. Three separate condensation reactions are involved in producing a triglyceride.

Triglyceride   Water

Saturated and Unsaturated Fatty Acids

Fatty acids are a major component of neutral fats and phospholipids. About 30 different kinds are found in animal lipids. **Saturated fatty acids** contain the maximum number of hydrogen atoms. **Unsaturated fatty acids** contain some carbon atoms that are double-bonded with each other and are not fully saturated with hydrogens. Lipids containing a high proportion of saturated fatty acids tend to be solids at room temperature (e.g. butter). Lipids with a high proportion of unsaturated fatty acids are oils and tend to be liquid at room temperature. This is because the unsaturation causes kinks in the straight chains so that the fatty acids do not pack closely together. Regardless of their degree of saturation, fatty acids yield a large amount of energy when oxidised.

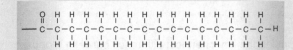

Formula (above) and molecular model (below) for **palmitic acid** (a saturated fatty acid)

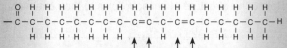

Formula (above) and molecular model (below) for **linoleic acid** (an unsaturated fatty acid)

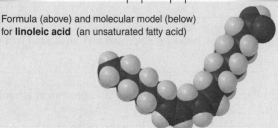

Phospholipids

Phospholipids are the main component of cellular membranes. They consist of a glycerol attached to two fatty acid chains and a phosphate (PO_4^{3-}) group. The phosphate end of the molecule is attracted to water (it is hydrophilic) while the fatty acid end is repelled (hydrophobic). The hydrophobic ends turn inwards in the membrane to form a **phospholipid bilayer**.

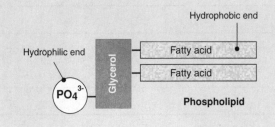

Steroids

Although steroids are classified as lipids, their structure is quite different from that of other lipids. Steroids have a basic structure of three rings made of 6 carbon atoms each and a fourth ring containing 5 carbon atoms. Examples of steroids include the male and female sex hormones (testosterone and oestrogen), and the hormones cortisol and aldosterone. Cholesterol, while not a steroid itself, is a sterol lipid and is a precursor to several steroid hormones.

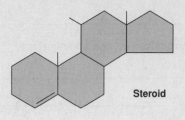

Steroid

Molecules of Life

Code: A 2

Important Biological Functions of Lipids

Lipids are concentrated sources of energy and provide fuel for aerobic respiration.

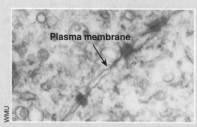

Phospholipids form the structural framework of cellular membranes.

Plasma membrane

Waxes and oils secreted on to surfaces provide waterproofing in plants and animals.

Fat absorbs shocks. Organs that are prone to bumps and shocks (e.g. kidneys) are cushioned with a relatively thick layer of fat.

Lipids are a source of metabolic water. During respiration, stored lipids are metabolised for energy, producing water and carbon dioxide.

Stored lipids provide insulation. Increased body fat reduces the amount of heat lost to the environment (e.g. in winter or in water).

1. Outline the key **chemical** difference between a phospholipid and a triglyceride: _____

_____

_____

2. Name the type of fatty acids found in lipids that form the following at room temperature:

   (a) Solid fats: _____ (b) Oils: _____

3. Relate the structure of phospholipids to their chemical properties and their functional role in cellular membranes:

_____

_____

4. (a) Distinguish between saturated and unsaturated fatty acids: _____

_____

   (b) Explain how the type of fatty acid present in a neutral fat or phospholipid is related to that molecule's properties:

_____

_____

   (c) Suggest how the cell membrane structure of an Arctic fish might differ from that of tropical fish species:

_____

_____

5. Identify two examples of steroids. For each example, describe its physiological function:

   (a) _____

   (b) _____

6. Explain how fats can provide an animal with:

   (a) Energy: _____

   (b) Water: _____

   (c) Insulation: _____

Nucleic Acids

Nucleic acids are a special group of chemicals in cells concerned with the transmission of inherited information. They have the capacity to store the information that controls cellular activity. The central nucleic acid is called **deoxyribonucleic acid** (DNA). DNA is a major component of chromosomes and is found primarily in the nucleus, although a small amount is found in mitochondria and chloroplasts. Other **ribonucleic acids** (RNA) are involved in the 'reading' of the DNA information. All nucleic acids are made up of simple repeating units called **nucleotides**, linked together to form chains or strands, often of great length (see the activity *DNA Molecules*). The strands vary in the sequence of the bases found on each nucleotide. It is this sequence which provides the 'genetic code' for the cell. In addition to nucleic acids, certain nucleotides and their derivatives are also important as suppliers of energy (**ATP**) or as hydrogen ion and electron carriers in respiration and photosynthesis (NAD, NADP, and FAD).

Chemical Structure of a Nucleotide

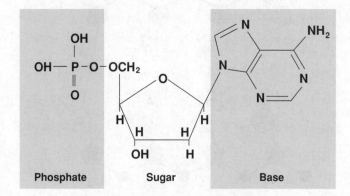

Phosphate Sugar Base

Symbolic Form of a Nucleotide

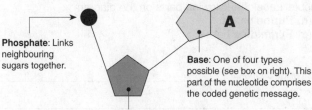

Phosphate: Links neighbouring sugars together.

Base: One of four types possible (see box on right). This part of the nucleotide comprises the coded genetic message.

Sugar: One of two types possible: ribose in RNA and deoxyribose in DNA.

Nucleotides are the building blocks of DNA. Their precise sequence in a DNA molecule provides the genetic instructions for the organism to which it governs. Accidental changes in nucleotide sequences are a cause of mutations, usually harming the organism, but occasionally providing benefits.

Bases

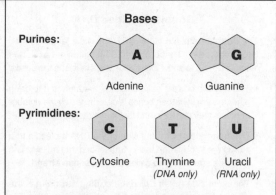

Purines: Adenine Guanine

Pyrimidines: Cytosine Thymine *(DNA only)* Uracil *(RNA only)*

The two-ringed bases above are **purines** and make up the longer bases. The single-ringed bases are **pyrimidines**. Although only one of four kinds of base can be used in a nucleotide, **uracil** is found only in RNA, replacing **thymine**. DNA contains: A, T, G, and C, while RNA contains A, U, G, and C.

Sugars

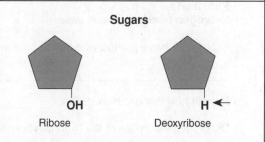

Ribose Deoxyribose

Deoxyribose sugar is found only in DNA. It differs from **ribose** sugar, found in RNA, by the lack of a single oxygen atom (arrowed).

Molecules of Life

RNA Molecule

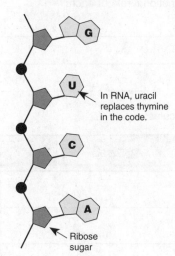

In RNA, uracil replaces thymine in the code.

Ribose sugar

DNA Molecule

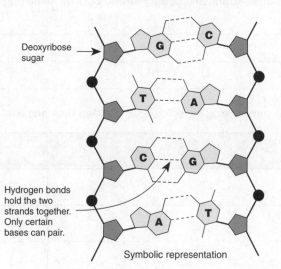

Deoxyribose sugar

Hydrogen bonds hold the two strands together. Only certain bases can pair.

Symbolic representation

DNA Molecule

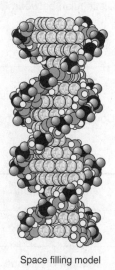

Space filling model

Ribonucleic acid (RNA) comprises a *single strand* of nucleotides linked together.

Deoxyribonucleic acid (DNA) comprises a *double strand* of nucleotides linked together. It is shown unwound in the symbolic representation (left). The DNA molecule takes on a twisted, double helix shape as shown in the space filling model on the right.

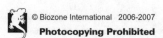

Code: A 1

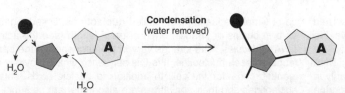

Formation of a nucleotide

Condensation
(water removed)

H_2O

H_2O

A nucleotide is formed when phosphoric acid and a base are chemically bonded to a sugar molecule. In both cases, water is given off, and they are therefore condensation reactions. In the reverse reaction, a nucleotide is broken apart by the addition of water (**hydrolysis**).

Formation of a dinucleotide

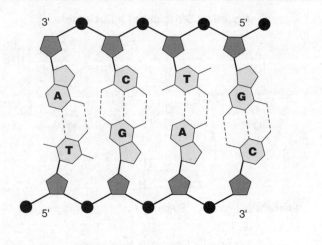

H_2O

Two nucleotides are linked together by a condensation reaction between the phosphate of one nucleotide and the sugar of another.

Double-Stranded DNA

The **double-helix** structure of DNA is like a ladder twisted into a corkscrew shape around its longitudinal axis. It is 'unwound' here to show the relationships between the bases.

• The way the correct pairs of bases are attracted to each other to form hydrogen bonds is determined by the number of bonds they can form and the shape (length) of the base.

• The **template strand** the side of the DNA molecule that stores the information that is transcribed into mRNA. The template strand is also called the **antisense strand**.

• The other side (often called the **coding strand**) has the same nucleotide sequence as the mRNA except that T in DNA substitutes for U in mRNA. The coding strand is also called the **sense strand**.

1. The diagram above depicts a double-stranded DNA molecule. Label the following parts on the diagram:
   (a) **Sugar** (deoxyribose)
   (b) **Phosphate**
   (c) **Hydrogen bonds** (between bases)
   (d) **Purine** bases
   (e) **Pyrimidine** bases

2. (a) Explain the **base-pairing rule** that applies in double-stranded DNA: _____

   _____

   (b) Explain how this differs in mRNA: _____

   (c) Describe the purpose of the hydrogen bonds in double-stranded DNA: _____

   _____

3. Describe the functional role of nucleotides: _____

   _____

4. Distinguish between the **template strand** and **coding strand** of DNA, identifying the functional role of each:

   _____

   _____

   _____

5. Complete the following table summarising the differences between DNA and RNA molecules:

	DNA	RNA
Sugar present		
Bases present		
Number of strands		
Relative length		

Amino Acids

Amino acids are the basic units from which proteins are made. Plants can manufacture all the amino acids they require from simpler molecules, but animals must obtain a certain number of ready-made amino acids (called **essential amino acids**) from their diet. The distinction between essential and non-essential amino acids is somewhat unclear though, as some amino acids can be produced from others and some are interconvertible by the urea cycle. Amino acids can combine to form peptide chains in a **condensation reaction**. The reverse reaction, the hydrolysis of peptide chains, releases free water and single amino acids.

Structure of Amino Acids

There are over 150 amino acids found in cells, but only 20 occur commonly in proteins. The remaining, non-protein amino acids have specialised roles as intermediates in metabolic reactions, or as neurotransmitters and hormones. All amino acids have a common structure (see right). The only difference between the different types lies with the 'R' group in the general formula. This group is variable, which means that it is different in each kind of amino acid.

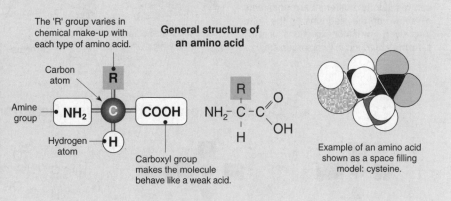

The 'R' group varies in chemical make-up with each type of amino acid.

General structure of an amino acid

Carbon atom

Amine group

Hydrogen atom

Carboxyl group makes the molecule behave like a weak acid.

Example of an amino acid shown as a space filling model: cysteine.

Properties of Amino Acids

Three examples of amino acids with different chemical properties are shown right, with their specific 'R' groups outlined. The 'R' groups can have quite diverse chemical properties.

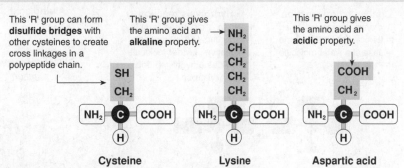

This 'R' group can form **disulfide bridges** with other cysteines to create cross linkages in a polypeptide chain.

This 'R' group gives the amino acid an **alkaline** property.

This 'R' group gives the amino acid an **acidic** property.

Cysteine   **Lysine**   **Aspartic acid**

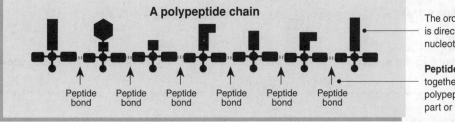

A polypeptide chain

Peptide bond · Peptide bond · Peptide bond · Peptide bond · Peptide bond · Peptide bond

The order of amino acids in a protein is directed by the order of nucleotides in DNA and mRNA.

Peptide bonds link amino acids together in long polymers called polypeptide chains. These may form part or all of a protein.

The amino acids are linked together by peptide bonds to form long chains of up to several hundred amino acids (called polypeptide chains). These chains may be functional units (complete by themselves) or they may need to be joined to other polypeptide chains before they can carry out their function. In humans, not all amino acids can be manufactured by our body: ten must be taken in with our diet (eight in adults). These are the 'essential amino acids'. They are indicated by the symbol ◆ on the right. Those indicated with as asterisk are also required by infants.

Amino acids occurring in proteins

Alanine	Glycine	Proline
Arginine *	Histidine *	Serine
Asparagine	Isoleucine ◆	Threonine ◆
Aspartic acid	Leucine ◆	Tryptophan ◆
Cysteine	Lysine ◆	Tyrosine
Glutamine	Methionine ◆	Valine ◆
Glutamic acid	Phenylalanine ◆	

1. Describe the biological function of amino acids: _____

_____

_____

_____

2. Describe what makes each of the 20 amino acids found in proteins unique: _____

_____

_____

_____

Molecules of Life

Code: A 2

Optical Isomers of Amino Acids

All amino acids, apart from the simplest one (glycine) show optical isomerism. The two forms that these optical isomers can take relate to the arrangement of the four bonding sites on the carbon atom. This can result in two different arrangements as shown on the diagrams on the right. With a very few minor exceptions, only the **L-forms** are found in living organisms.

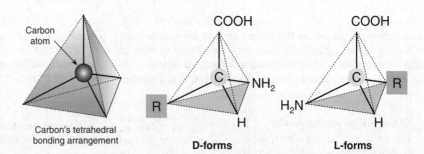

Carbon atom

Carbon's tetrahedral bonding arrangement

D-forms

L-forms

Condensation and Hydrolysis Reactions

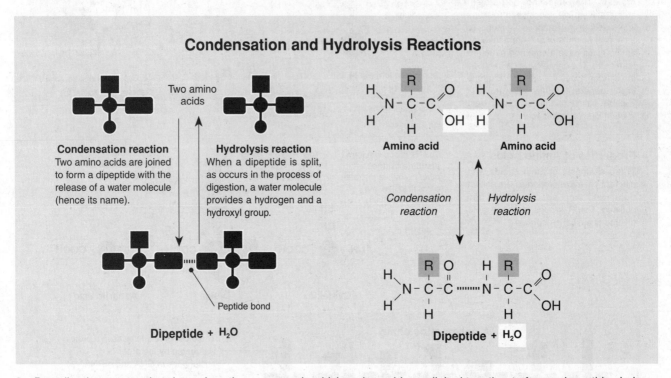

Condensation reaction
Two amino acids are joined to form a dipeptide with the release of a water molecule (hence its name).

Hydrolysis reaction
When a dipeptide is split, as occurs in the process of digestion, a water molecule provides a hydrogen and a hydroxyl group.

Peptide bond

Dipeptide + H₂O

Amino acid   Amino acid

Condensation reaction   *Hydrolysis reaction*

Dipeptide + H₂O

3. Describe the process that determines the sequence in which amino acids are linked together to form polypeptide chains:

_____

_____

4. Explain what is meant by **essential amino acids**: _____

_____

_____

5. Describe briefly the process of the **condensation** reaction for amino acids: _____

_____

_____

_____

_____

6. Describe briefly the process of the **hydrolysis** reaction for amino acids: _____

_____

_____

_____

_____

7. Name the optical isomeric form that occurs in nearly all amino acids in living things: _____

Proteins

The precise folding up of a protein into its **tertiary structure** creates a three dimensional arrangement of the active 'R' groups. The way each 'R' group faces with respect to the others gives the protein its unique chemical properties. If a protein loses this precise structure (denaturation), it is usually unable to carry out its biological function. Proteins are often classified on the basis of structure (globular vs fibrous). Some of the properties used for the basis of structural classification are outlined over the page.

Primary Structure - 1° *(amino acid sequence)*

Strings of hundreds of amino acids link together with peptide bonds to form molecules called polypeptide chains. There are 20 different kinds of amino acids that can be linked together in a vast number of different combinations. This sequence is called the **primary structure**. It is the arrangement of attraction and repulsion points in the amino acid chain that determines the higher levels of organisation in the protein and its biological function.

Secondary Structure - 2° *(α-helix or ß pleated sheet)*

Polypeptides become folded in various ways, referred to as the secondary (2°) structure. The most common types of 2° structures are a coiled α-**helix** and a β-**pleated sheet**. Secondary structures are maintained with hydrogen bonds between neighbouring CO and NH groups. H-bonds, although individually weak, provide considerable strength when there are a large number of them. The example, right, shows the two main types of secondary structure. In both, the **'R' side groups** (not shown) project out from the structure. Most globular proteins contain regions of α-helices together with β-sheets. Keratin (a fibrous protein) is composed almost entirely of α-helices. Fibroin (silk protein), is another fibrous protein, almost entirely in β-sheet form.

Tertiary Structure - 3° *(folding)*

Every protein has a precise structure formed by the folding of the secondary structure into a complex shape called the **tertiary structure**. The protein folds up because various points on the secondary structure are attracted to one another. The strongest links are caused by bonding between neighbouring *cysteine* amino acids which form disulfide bridges. Other interactions that are involved in folding include weak ionic and hydrogen bonds as well as hydrophobic interactions.

Quaternary Structure - 4°

Some proteins (such as enzymes) are complete and functional with a tertiary structure only. However, many complex proteins exist as aggregations of polypeptide chains. The arrangement of the polypeptide chains into a functional protein is termed the **quaternary structure**. The example (right) shows a molecule of haemoglobin, a globular protein composed of 4 polypeptide sub-units joined together; two identical *beta chains* and two identical *alpha chains*. Each has a haem (iron containing) group at the centre of the chain, which binds oxygen. Proteins containing non-protein material are **conjugated proteins**. The non-protein part is the **prosthetic group**.

Denaturation of Proteins

Denaturation refers to the loss of the three-dimensional structure (and usually also the biological function) of a protein. Denaturation is often, although not always, permanent. It results from an alteration of the bonds that maintain the secondary and tertiary structure of the protein, even though the sequence of amino acids remains unchanged. Agents that cause denaturation are:

- **Strong acids and alkalis**: Disrupt ionic bonds and result in coagulation of the protein. Long exposure also breaks down the primary structure of the protein.
- **Heavy metals**: May disrupt ionic bonds, form strong bonds with the carboxyl groups of the R groups, and reduce protein charge. The general effect is to cause the precipitation of the protein.
- **Heat and radiation** (e.g. UV): Cause disruption of the bonds in the protein through increased energy provided to the atoms.
- **Detergents and solvents**: Form bonds with the non-polar groups in the protein, thereby disrupting hydrogen bonding.

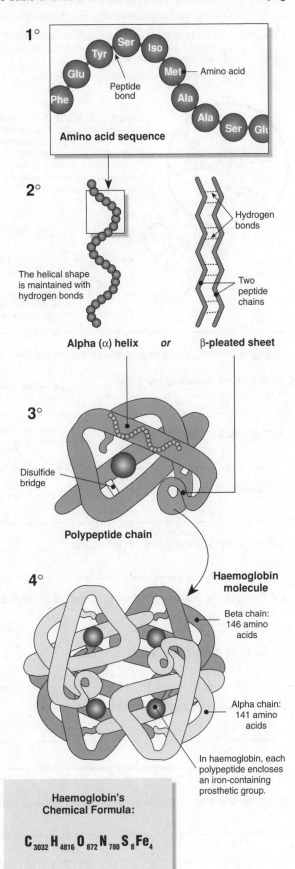

1°
Tyr Ser Iso
Glu Met — Amino acid
Phe Ala
Peptide bond
Ala
Ser Glu
Amino acid sequence

2°
The helical shape is maintained with hydrogen bonds
Hydrogen bonds
Two peptide chains
Alpha (α) helix *or* **β-pleated sheet**

3°
Disulfide bridge
Polypeptide chain

Haemoglobin molecule

4°
Beta chain: 146 amino acids
Alpha chain: 141 amino acids
In haemoglobin, each polypeptide encloses an iron-containing prosthetic group.

Haemoglobin's Chemical Formula:

$$C_{3032} H_{4816} O_{872} N_{780} S_8 Fe_4$$

Molecules of Life

Code: RA 2

22

Structural Classification of Proteins

Fibrous Proteins

Properties
- Water insoluble
- Very tough physically; may be supple or stretchy
- Parallel polypeptide chains in long fibres or sheets

Function
- Structural role in cells and organisms *e.g. collagen found in connective tissue, cartilage, bones, tendons, and blood vessel walls.*
- Contractile *e.g. myosin, actin*

Globular Proteins

Properties
- Easily water soluble
- Tertiary structure critical to function
- Polypeptide chains folded into a spherical shape

Function
- Catalytic *e.g. enzymes*
- Regulatory *e.g. hormones (insulin)*
- Transport *e.g. haemoglobin*
- Protective *e.g. antibodies*

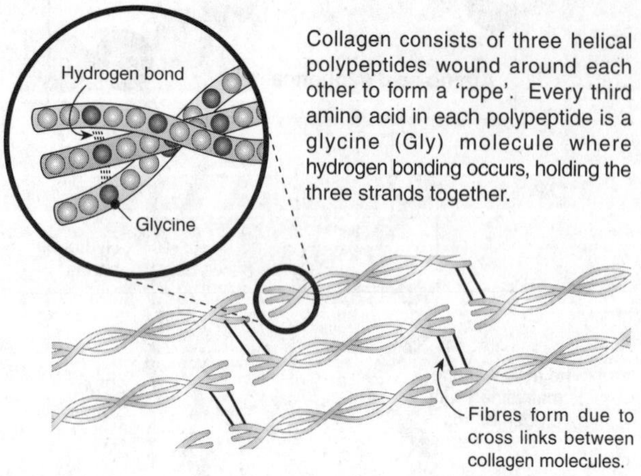

Collagen consists of three helical polypeptides wound around each other to form a 'rope'. Every third amino acid in each polypeptide is a glycine (Gly) molecule where hydrogen bonding occurs, holding the three strands together.

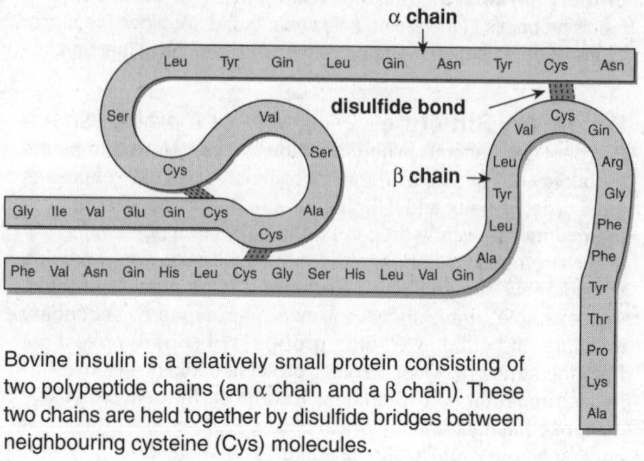

Fibres form due to cross links between collagen molecules.

Bovine insulin is a relatively small protein consisting of two polypeptide chains (an α chain and a β chain). These two chains are held together by disulfide bridges between neighbouring cysteine (Cys) molecules.

1. Giving examples, briefly explain how proteins are involved in the following functional roles:

(a) Structural tissues of the body: _____

(b) Regulating body processes: _____

(c) Contractile elements: _____

(d) Immunological response to pathogens: _____

(e) Transporting molecules within cells and in the bloodstream: _____

(f) Catalysing metabolic reactions in cells: _____

2. Explain how denaturation destroys protein function: _____

3. Describe one structural difference between globular and fibrous proteins: _____

4. Determine the total number of amino acids in the α and β chains of the insulin molecule illustrated above:

(a) α chain: _____ (b) β chain: _____

Modification of Proteins

Proteins may be modified after they have been produced by ribosomes. After they pass into the interior of rough endoplasmic reticulum, some proteins may have carbohydrates added to them to form **glycoproteins**. Proteins may be further altered in the Golgi apparatus. The **Golgi apparatus** functions principally as a system for processing, sorting, and modifying proteins. Proteins that are to be secreted from the cell are synthesised by ribosomes on the rough endoplasmic reticulum and transported to the Golgi apparatus. At this stage, carbohydrates may be removed or added in a step-wise process. Some of the possible functions of glycoproteins are illustrated below. Other proteins may have fatty acids added to them to form **lipoproteins**. These modified proteins transport lipids in the plasma between various organs in the body (e.g. gut, liver, and adipose tissue).

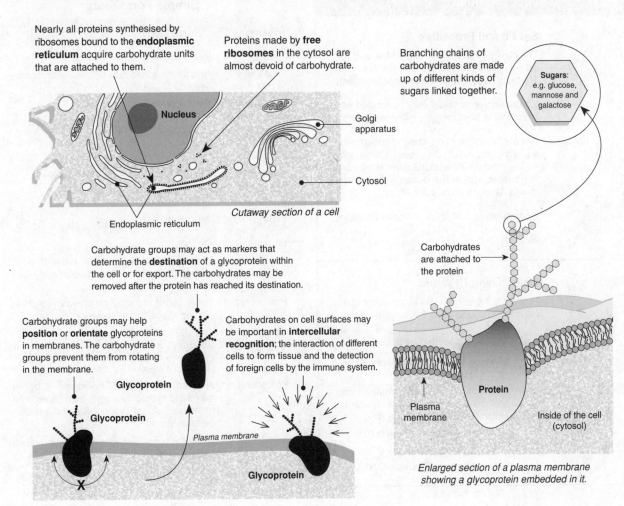

Nearly all proteins synthesised by ribosomes bound to the **endoplasmic reticulum** acquire carbohydrate units that are attached to them.

Proteins made by **free ribosomes** in the cytosol are almost devoid of carbohydrate.

Branching chains of carbohydrates are made up of different kinds of sugars linked together.

Sugars: e.g. glucose, mannose and galactose

Nucleus

Golgi apparatus

Cytosol

Cutaway section of a cell

Endoplasmic reticulum

Carbohydrate groups may act as markers that determine the **destination** of a glycoprotein within the cell or for export. The carbohydrates may be removed after the protein has reached its destination.

Carbohydrate groups may help **position** or **orientate** glycoproteins in membranes. The carbohydrate groups prevent them from rotating in the membrane.

Glycoprotein

Glycoprotein

Plasma membrane

Carbohydrates on cell surfaces may be important in **intercellular recognition**; the interaction of different cells to form tissue and the detection of foreign cells by the immune system.

Glycoprotein

Carbohydrates are attached to the protein

Protein

Plasma membrane

Inside of the cell (cytosol)

Enlarged section of a plasma membrane showing a glycoprotein embedded in it.

Molecules of Life

1. (a) Explain what a **glycoprotein** is: _____

   (b) Briefly describe three **roles** of glycoproteins: _____

   _____

   _____

2. (a) Explain what a **lipoprotein** is: _____

   (b) Briefly describe the **role** of lipoproteins: _____

   _____

   _____

3. Suggest why proteins made by free ribosomes in the cytosol are usually free of carbohydrate: _____

   _____

4. Suggest why the orientation of a protein in the plasma membrane might be important: _____

   _____

   _____

Code: A 2

Biochemical Tests

Biochemical tests are used to detect the presence of nutrients such as lipids, proteins, and carbohydrates (sugar and starch) in various foods. These simple tests are useful for detecting nutrients when large quantities are present. A more accurate technique by which to separate a mixture of compounds involves chromatography. Chromatography is used when only a small sample is available or when you wish to distinguish between nutrients. Simple biochemical food tests will show whether sugar is present, whereas chromatography will distinguish between the different types of sugars (e.g. fructose or glucose).

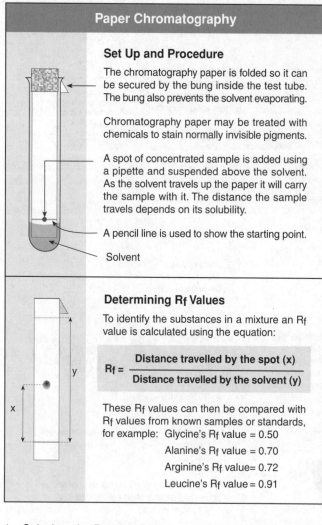

Paper Chromatography

Set Up and Procedure

The chromatography paper is folded so it can be secured by the bung inside the test tube. The bung also prevents the solvent evaporating.

Chromatography paper may be treated with chemicals to stain normally invisible pigments.

A spot of concentrated sample is added using a pipette and suspended above the solvent. As the solvent travels up the paper it will carry the sample with it. The distance the sample travels depends on its solubility.

A pencil line is used to show the starting point.

Solvent

Determining R_f Values

To identify the substances in a mixture an R_f value is calculated using the equation:

$$R_f = \frac{\text{Distance travelled by the spot (x)}}{\text{Distance travelled by the solvent (y)}}$$

These R_f values can then be compared with R_f values from known samples or standards, for example: Glycine's R_f value = 0.50

Alanine's R_f value = 0.70

Arginine's R_f value= 0.72

Leucine's R_f value = 0.91

Simple Food Tests

Proteins: The Biuret Test

Reagent:	Biuret solution.
Procedure:	A sample is added to biuret solution and gently heated.
Positive result:	Solution turns from blue to lilac.

Starch: The Iodine Test

Reagent:	Iodine.
Procedure:	Iodine solution is added to the sample.
Positive result:	Blue-black staining occurs.

Lipids: The Emulsion Test

Reagent:	Ethanol.
Procedure:	The sample is shaken with ethanol. After settling, the liquid portion is distilled and mixed with water.
Positive result:	The solution turns into a cloudy-white emulsion of suspended lipid molecules.

Sugars: The Benedict's Test

Reagent:	Benedict's solution.
Procedure:	*Non reducing sugars*: The sample is boiled with dilute hydrochloric acid, then cooled and neutralised. A test for reducing sugars is then performed.
	Reducing sugar: Benedict's solution is added, and the sample is placed in a water bath.
Positive result:	Solution turns from blue to orange.

1. Calculate the R_f value for the example given above (show your working): _____

   _____

2. Explain why the R_f value of a substance is always less than 1: _____

   _____

3. Discuss when it is appropriate to use chromatography instead of a simple food test: _____

   _____

   _____

4. Predict what would happen if a sample was immersed in the chromatography solvent, instead of suspended above it:

   _____

   _____

5. With reference to their R_f values, rank the four amino acids (listed above) in terms of their solubility: _____

   _____

6. Outline why lipids must be mixed in ethanol before they will form an emulsion in water: _____

   _____

Enzymes

Most enzymes are proteins. They are capable of catalysing (speeding up) biochemical reactions and are therefore called biological **catalysts**. Enzymes act on one or more compounds (called the **substrate**). They may break a single substrate molecule down into simpler substances, or join two or more substrate molecules chemically together. The enzyme itself is unchanged in the reaction; its presence merely allows the reaction to take place more rapidly. When the substrate attains the required **activation energy** to enable it to change into the product, there is a 50% chance that it will proceed forward to form the product, otherwise it reverts back to a stable form of the reactant again. The part of the enzyme's surface into which the substrate is bound and undergoes reaction is known as the **active site**. This is made of different parts of polypeptide chain folded in a specific shape so they are closer together. For some enzymes, the complexity of the binding sites can be very precise, allowing only a single kind of substrate to bind to it. Some other enzymes have lower **specificity** and will accept a wide range of substrates of the same general type (e.g. lipases break up any fatty acid chain length of lipid). This is because the enzyme is specific for the type of chemical bond involved and not an exact substrate.

Enzyme Structure

The model on the right is of an enzyme called *Ribonuclease S*, that breaks up RNA molecules. It is a typical enzyme, being a globular protein and composed of up to several hundred atoms. The darkly shaded areas are called **active sites** and make up the **cleft**; the region into which the substrate molecule(s) are drawn. The correct positioning of these sites is critical for the catalytic reaction to occur. The substrate (RNA in this case) is drawn into the cleft by the active sites. By doing so, it puts the substrate molecule under stress, causing the reaction to proceed more readily.

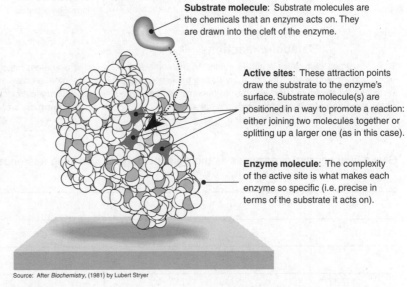

Substrate molecule: Substrate molecules are the chemicals that an enzyme acts on. They are drawn into the cleft of the enzyme.

Active sites: These attraction points draw the substrate to the enzyme's surface. Substrate molecule(s) are positioned in a way to promote a reaction: either joining two molecules together or splitting up a larger one (as in this case).

Enzyme molecule: The complexity of the active site is what makes each enzyme so specific (i.e. precise in terms of the substrate it acts on).

Source: After *Biochemistry*, (1981) by Lubert Stryer

How Enzymes Work

The **lock and key** model proposed earlier this century suggested that the substrate was simply drawn into a closely matching cleft on the enzyme molecule. More recent studies have revealed that the process more likely involves an **induced fit** (see diagram on the right), where the enzyme or the reactants change their shape slightly. The reactants become bound to enzymes by weak chemical bonds. This binding can weaken bonds within the reactants themselves, allowing the reaction to proceed more readily.

 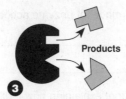

1 Enzyme   **Substrate**   **2**   **3**   **Products**

The presence of an enzyme simply makes it easier for a reaction to take place. All **catalysts** speed up reactions by influencing the stability of bonds in the reactants. They may also provide an alternative reaction pathway, thus lowering the activation energy needed for a reaction to take place (see the graph below).

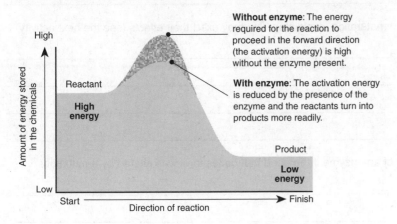

Without enzyme: The energy required for the reaction to proceed in the forward direction (the activation energy) is high without the enzyme present.

With enzyme: The activation energy is reduced by the presence of the enzyme and the reactants turn into products more readily.

Induced Fit Model

An enzyme fits to its substrate somewhat like a lock and key. The shape of the enzyme changes when the substrate fits into the cleft (called the **induced fit**):

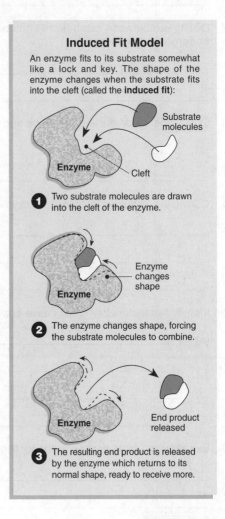

Substrate molecules

Enzyme — Cleft

1 Two substrate molecules are drawn into the cleft of the enzyme.

Enzyme changes shape

Enzyme

2 The enzyme changes shape, forcing the substrate molecules to combine.

Enzyme

End product released

3 The resulting end product is released by the enzyme which returns to its normal shape, ready to receive more.

Molecules of Life

Code: RA 2

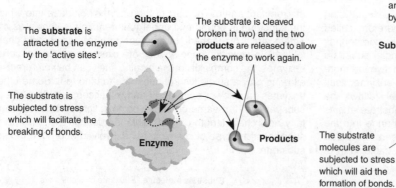

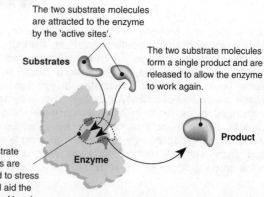

Catabolic reactions

Some enzymes can cause a single substrate molecule to be drawn into the active site. Chemical bonds are broken, causing the substrate molecule to break apart to become two separate molecules. **Examples**: *digestion, cellular respiration*.

Anabolic reactions

Some enzymes can cause two substrate molecules to be drawn into the active site. Chemical bonds are formed, causing the two substrate molecules to form bonds and become a single molecule. **Examples**: *protein synthesis, photosynthesis*.

1. Give a brief account of enzymes as **biological catalysts**, including reference to the role of the **active site**:

   _____

   _____

   _____

   _____

   _____

2. Distinguish between **catabolism** and **anabolism**, giving an example of each and identifying each reaction as **endergonic** or **exergonic**:

   _____

   _____

   _____

3. Outline the key features of the '**lock and key**' model of enzyme action: _____

   _____

   _____

4. Outline the '**induced fit**' model of enzyme action, explaining how it differs from the lock and key model:

   _____

   _____

   _____

5. Identify two factors that could cause enzyme denaturation, explaining how they exert their effects (see the next activity):

   (a) _____

   _____

   (b) _____

   _____

6. Explain what might happen to the functioning of an enzyme if the gene that codes for it was altered by a mutation:

   _____

   _____

Enzyme Reaction Rates

Enzymes are sensitive molecules. They often have a narrow range of conditions under which they operate properly. For most of the enzymes associated with plant and animal metabolism, there is little activity at low temperatures. As the temperature increases, so too does the enzyme activity, until the point is reached where the temperature is high enough to damage the enzyme's structure. At this point, the enzyme ceases to function; a phenomenon called enzyme or protein **denaturation**.

Extremes in acidity (pH) can also cause the protein structure of enzymes to denature. Poisons often work by denaturing enzymes or occupying the enzyme's active site so that it does not function. In some cases, enzymes will not function without cofactors, such as vitamins or trace elements. In the four graphs below, the *rate of reaction* or *degree of enzyme activity* is plotted against each of four factors that affect enzyme performance. Answer the questions relating to each graph:

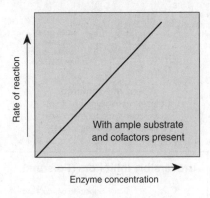

1. **Enzyme concentration**
   (a) Describe the change in the rate of reaction when the enzyme concentration is increased (assuming there is plenty of the substrate present):

   _____

   _____

   (b) Suggest how a cell may vary the amount of enzyme present in a cell:

   _____

   _____

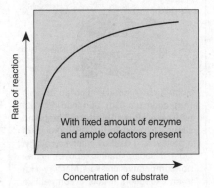

2. **Substrate concentration**
   (a) Describe the change in the rate of reaction when the substrate concentration is **increased** (assuming a fixed amount of enzyme and ample cofactors):

   _____

   _____

   (b) Explain why the rate changes the way it does: _____

   _____

   _____

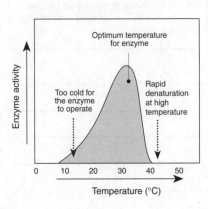

3. **Temperature**
   Higher temperatures speed up all reactions, but few enzymes can tolerate temperatures higher than 50–60°C. The rate at which enzymes are **denatured** (change their shape and become inactive) increases with higher temperatures.

   (a) Describe what is meant by an optimum temperature for enzyme activity:

   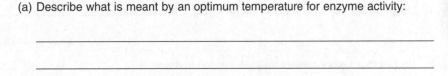

   (b) Explain why most enzymes perform poorly at low temperatures:

   _____

   _____

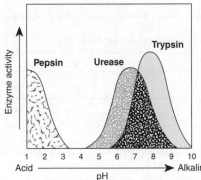

4. **pH (acidity/alkalinity)**
   Like all proteins, enzymes are **denatured** by extremes of **pH** (very acid or alkaline). Within these extremes, most enzymes are still influenced by pH. Each enzyme has a preferred pH range for optimum activity.

   (a) State the optimum pH for each of the enzymes:

   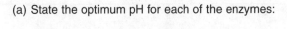
   Pepsin: _____   Trypsin: _____   Urease: _____

   (b) Pepsin acts on proteins in the stomach. Explain how its optimum pH is suited to its working environment:

   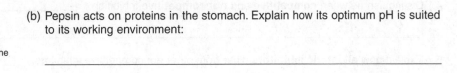

Molecules of Life

Code: RDA 2

Enzyme Cofactors and Inhibitors

Enzyme activity is often influenced by the presence of other chemicals. Some of these may enhance an enzyme's activity. Called **cofactors**, they are a nonprotein component of an enzyme and may be organic molecules (**coenzymes**) or inorganic ions (e.g. Ca^{2+}, Zn^{2+}). Enzymes may also be deactivated, temporarily or permanently, by chemicals called enzyme **inhibitors**.

Types of Enzyme

Nearly all enzymes are made of protein, although RNA has been demonstrated to have enzymatic properties. Some enzymes consist of just protein, while others require the addition of extra components to complete their catalytic properties. These may be permanently attached parts called **prosthetic groups**, or temporarily attached pieces (**coenzymes**) that detach after a reaction, and may participate with another enzyme in other reactions.

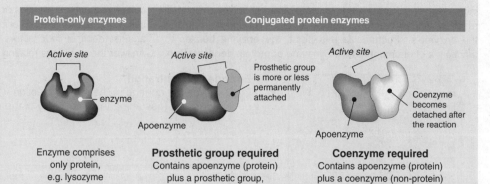

Protein-only enzymes

Enzyme comprises only protein, e.g. lysozyme

Conjugated protein enzymes

Prosthetic group required
Contains apoenzyme (protein) plus a prosthetic group, e.g. flavoprotein + FAD

Coenzyme required
Contains apoenzyme (protein) plus a coenzyme (non-protein) e.g. dehydrogenases + NAD

Reversible Enzyme Inhibitors

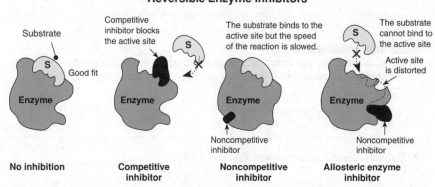

No inhibition   **Competitive inhibitor**   **Noncompetitive inhibitor**   **Allosteric enzyme inhibitor**

Enzyme inhibitors may be reversible or irreversible. **Reversible inhibitors** are used to control enzyme activity. There is often an interaction between the substrate or end product and the enzymes controlling the reaction. Buildup of the end product or a lack of substrate may deactivate the enzyme. This deactivation may take the form of **competitive** (competes for the active site) or **noncompetitive** inhibition. While noncompetitive inhibitors have the effect of slowing down the rate of reaction, **allosteric inhibitors** block the active site altogether and prevent its functioning.

Irreversible Inhibitors (Poisons)

Some heavy metals, such as arsenic (As), cadmium (Cd), and lead (Pb) act as **irreversible inhibitors**. They bind strongly to the sulfhydryl (-SH) groups of a protein and destroy catalytic activity. Most, including arsenic (above), act as **noncompetitive** inhibitors. Mercury (Hg) is an exception; it acts a competitive inhibitor, binding to the sulfhydryl group in the active site of the papain enzyme. Heavy metals are retained in the body and lost slowly.

1. Describe the general role of **cofactors** in enzyme activity: _____

_____

2. (a) List four **heavy metals** that are toxic to humans: _____

(b) Explain in general terms why these heavy metals are toxic to life: _____

_____

3. There are many enzyme inhibitors that are not heavy metals (e.g. those found in some pesticides).

(a) Name a **common poison** that is an enzyme inhibitor, but not a heavy metal: _____

(b) Try to find out how this poison interferes with enzyme function. Briefly describe its effect on a named enzyme:

_____

_____

4. Distinguish between **competitive** and **noncompetitive** inhibition: _____

_____

5. Explain how **allosteric inhibitors** differ from other noncompetitive inhibitors: _____

_____

Cell Structure

The structure and features of cells

Cell theory, cell ultrastructure, microscopy. Tissues and organs, cellular environments and separating cellular components.

Learning Objectives

☐ 1. Compile your own glossary from the **KEY WORDS** displayed in **bold type** in the learning objectives below.

Cell Theory *(page 31)*

☐ 2. Define the **cell theory**. Recognise the contribution of microscopy to the development of cell theory and our present knowledge of cell structure.

Features of Cells *(pages 32-48, 49-53, 61)*

☐ 3. Define a **cell** and recognise it as the basic unit of living things. In simple terms, describe the main features of a cell (**plasma membrane, cytoplasm, organelles**). Identify the features that characterise living things and explain why cells are considered to be living entities.

☐ 4. Use different units of measurement (mm, μm, nm) to express cell sizes and to describe a range of cell sizes.

☐ 5. Contrast the generalised structure of **prokaryote** and **eukaryote** cells and provide examples of each type. If required, describe the specific features of protoctistan and fungal cells. Explain clearly why **viruses** are regarded as non-cellular.

☐ 6. Describe the structure of a **bacterial cell** and its inclusions, as illustrated by a named example (e.g. *E. coli*). Identify the **bacterial cell wall** and the structures associated with it (**flagella**, pili), the **bacterial chromosome** and **plasmids**, the **plasma membrane**, glycogen granules, and lipid droplets. Recognise these structures in electron micrographs of bacterial cells and identify which of them are unique to prokaryotes.

☐ 7. Describe the general characteristics of **fungi**, as illustrated by representative **moulds** (e.g. *Pencillium*) and **yeasts** (e.g. *Saccharomyces*). Identify differences in structure between these two groups of fungi.

☐ 8. Describe and interpret drawings and photographs of typical **plant** and **animal cells** (e.g. leaf palisade cell and liver cell) as seen using light microscopy.

☐ 9. Describe and interpret drawings and photographs of typical plant and animal cells (e.g. leaf palisade cell and liver cell) as seen using electron microscopy. Identify the following:
   • **nucleus, nuclear envelope, nucleolus**
   • **mitochondria, chloroplasts** (if present),
   • rough/smooth **endoplasmic reticulum, ribosomes**,
   • **plasma membrane, cell wall** (if present)
   • **Golgi apparatus, lysosomes, vacuoles** (if present),
   • **cytoplasm, cytoskeleton** (of **microtubules**), **centrioles, cilia** (if present)
   Outline the role of each of these cell components.

☐ 10. Identify which of the cellular structures above would be visible under light microscopy, transmission electron microscopy, and scanning electron microscopy.

☐ 11. List the differences between plant and animal cells, noting relative size and shape, and presence or absence of particular structures and organelles.

Separating Cellular Components *(page 54)*

☐ 12. Describe the principles of **cell fractionation** (**differential centrifugation**). Explain how it is achieved through **homogenisation** of a sample followed by **ultracentrifugation**.

☐ 13. Identify the components of the four fractions normally obtained from differential centrifugation: the **nuclear fraction**, the **mitochondrial fraction**, the **microsomal fraction**, and the **soluble fraction**. Explain the role of speed of centrifugation in separating these fractions.

Cellular Environments *(pages 35-36)*

☐ 14. Describe the requirements of cells in terms of their immediate environment. Explain how an **optimum cellular environment** can be provided in the laboratory. Describe how this knowledge is applied in modern **tissue culture**.

☐ 15. Describe the features of some of the environments in which cells are found (e.g. aquatic, soil, body tissue). Describe the problems that cells must cope with in different environments. Explain why many bacteria are able to colonise inhospitable environments.

☐ 16. Distinguish between a single celled and a **multicellular organism**. With respect to the cellular environment, outline the benefits of being multicellular.

Microscopy *(pages 37-40)*

☐ 17. Distinguish between **optical** and **electron microscopes**, outlining the structure of each. With respect to light and electron microscopy, explain and distinguish between: **magnification** and **resolution**.

☐ 18. With respect to the basic microscope structure and operation, and type of image produced, distinguish between TEM (**transmission electron microscopy**) and SEM (**scanning electron microscopy**). Recognise electron microscopy as an important tool in investigating cell structure and function.

☐ 19. Distinguish between **compound** and **stereo light microscopes**. Identify the situations in which these different microscopes would be used.

☐ 20. Familiarise yourself with the use of a light microscope. Demonstrate an ability to correctly use a microscope to locate material and focus images.

☐ 21. List the steps required for preparing a **temporary mount** for viewing with a compound light microscope.

☐ 22. Demonstrate an ability to use simple **staining techniques** to show specific features of cells. Understand why **stains** are useful in the preparation of specimens. Demonstrate a knowledge of some specific stains, identifying the purpose of each named example.

Tissues and Organs *(pages 55-58, 95-96)*

☐ 23. Summarise how the **zygote** (fertilised egg) undergoes division to produce an adult. Define the terms: **cellular differentiation, specialised cell**. Comment on the basic similarity of cells early in development.

☐ 24. Recognise the hierarchy of organisation in multicellular organisms: *molecular, organelle, cell, tissue, organ.* With respect to the function of specialised cells, outline the benefits of being multicellular. Explain the terms: **tissue** and **organ**.

☐ 25. With reference to specific examples (e.g. epithelial tissues, blood, xylem, and/or phloem), explain *how* cells are organised into **tissues**.

☐ 26. Identify and describe the structural adaptations and function of some specialised cells in humans, e.g. blood cells, liver cells, or intestinal epithelial cells. For each cell type, identify the tissue where it occurs.

☐ 27. Identify and describe the structural adaptations and function of some of the specialised cell types found in angiosperm plant tissues, including the leaf palisade (mesophyll) cell. Categorise these into cells associated with the stem, roots, leaves, or reproductive structures.

☐ 28. Describe examples of tissues (e.g. xylem) and organs (e.g. leaves) in plants, identifying their functional role in each case. Illustrate your examples and calculate the linear magnification of your drawing in each case.

☐ 29. Describe examples of tissues (e.g. blood, epithelium) and organs (e.g. blood vessels, lung, small intestine, liver) in animals, identifying their functional role in each case. Illustrate your examples and calculate the linear magnification of your drawing in each case.

See page 7 for additional details of these texts:

■ Adds, J., *et al.*, 2003. **Molecules and Cells**, (NelsonThornes), chpt. 4.

■ Adds, J., *et al.*, 1999. **Tools, Techniques and Assessment in Biology**, (NelsonThornes), pp. 13-26.

■ Chenn, P. 1997. **Microorganisms and Biotechnology**, (John Murray), Chpt. 1.

■ Clegg, C.J., 1998. **Mammals: Structure and Function**, (John Murray), pp. 1, 4-7, 10-11.

■ Taylor, J., 2001. **Microorganisms and Biotechnology** (NelsonThornes), Chpt 2.

■ Tobin, A.J. and Morel, R.E., 1997. **Asking About Cells**, (Thomson Brooks/Cole), as required.

See page 7 for details of publishers of periodicals:

STUDENT'S REFERENCE

Microscopy and cell structure

■ **The Power Behind an Electron Microscopist** Biol. Sci. Rev., 18(1) Sept. 2005, pp. 16-20. *The principles of electron microscopy: how to recognise structures, magnification and scale, and the importance of 3D in interpreting cellular features.*

■ **Size Does Matter** Biol. Sci. Rev., 17 (3) February 2005, pp. 10-13. *Measuring the size of organisms and calculating magnification and scale.*

■ **Transmission Electron Microscopy** Biol. Sci. Rev., 13(2) November 2000, pp. 32-35. *An excellent account of the techniques and applications of TEM. Includes an excellent diagram comparing features of TEM and light microscopy.*

■ **X-Ray Microscopy** Biol. Sci. Rev., 14(2) November 2001, pp. 38-40. *A short account of the technique and application of X-ray microscopy. Its advantages over EM are explained, particularly with respect to specimen preparation.*

■ **Scanning Electron Microscopy** Biol. Sci. Rev., 20(1) Sept. 2007, pp. 38-41. *An excellent account of the techniques and applications of SEM. Includes details of specimen preparation and recent advancements in the technology.*

■ **Light Microscopy** Biol. Sci. Rev., 13(1) Sept. 2000, pp. 36-38. *An excellent account of the basis and various techniques of light microscopy.*

■ **Cellular Factories** New Scientist, 23 November 1996 (Inside Science). *The structure and role of organelles in plant and animal cells.*

■ **Control Centre** New Scientist, 17 July 1999 (Inside Science). *The nucleus: the organisation of DNA in eukaryotic cells, how genes code for proteins, and the function of ribosomes and RNA.*

■ **The Beat Goes On: Cilia and Flagella** Biol. Sci. Rev., 18(4) April 2006, pp. 2-6. *The structure and function of cilia and flagella and their important roles in biological systems.*

■ **Border Control** New Scientist, 15 July 2000 (Inside Science). *The role of the plasma membrane in cell function: membrane structure and transport, and the role of membrane receptors.*

■ **Lysosomes: The Cell's Recycling Centres** Biol. Sci. Rev., 17(2) Nov. 2004, pp. 21-23. *This account covers the nature and role of lysosomes: small membrane-bound organelles found in all eukaryotic cells.*

■ **Lysosomes and their Versatile and Potentially Fatal Membranes** Biol. Sci. Rev., 17(3) Feb. 2005, pp. 14-16. *This article discusses the critical importance of the lysosome membrane and considers the effects of lysosomes in disease.*

■ **No Visible Means of Support** Biol. Sci. Rev., 8(4) March 1996, pp. 6-10. *The role of the cell cytoskeleton in plant & animal growth and support.*

■ **Water Channels in the Cell Membrane** Biol. Sci. Rev., 9(2) November 1996, pp. 18-22. *The role of proteins in membrane transport, including mechanisms involved in physiological processes.*

■ **The Force** New Scientist, 26 February 2000, pp. 30-35. *An account of mitochondria and how they can exercise control over reproduction.*

Cell differentiation and tissues

■ **Connective Tissues** Biol. Sci. Rev., 8(1) September 1995, pp. 27-30. *The varied and numerous roles of connective tissues in the body (includes histological details).*

■ **Surface Epithelial Tissue** Biol. Sci. Rev., 7(1) September 1994, pp. 23-27. *The structure and function epithelial tissues (excellent).*

■ **Basement Membranes** Biol. Sci. Rev., 13(4) March 2001, pp. 36-39. *The structure, function, and diversity of basement membranes (including their pivotal role in the structure of tissues).*

TEACHER'S REFERENCE

■ **Are Viruses Alive?** Scientific American, Dec. 2004, pp. 77-81. *Although viruses challenge our concept of what "living" means, they are vital members of the web of life. An excellent account.*

■ **Secret Language of Cells** New Scientist, 16 Feb 2002 (Inside Science). *An article about communication between cells, including the role of gap junctions, hormones, ligands and receptors. It leads onto a discussion of how cell division is disrupted in cancer and following thalidomide use.*

■ **Bacteria** National Geographic, 184(2) August 1993, pp. 36-61. *Structure and diversity of bacteria: the most abundant and useful organisms on Earth.*

■ **Cells by Design** New Scientist, 3 June 1989, pp. 24-26. *Artificially produced cells have been made by simulating the plasma membrane and enclosing materials within.*

■ **The Machinery of Cell Crawling** Scientific American, September 1994, pp. 40-49. *Excellent article covering the complex ultrastructure that allows cells to move.*

■ **The Birth of Complex Cells** Scientific American, April 1996, pp. 38-45. *An excellent article covering the evolution of cell structure and the functions of various organelles.*

■ **The Architecture of Life** Scientific American, January 1998, pp. 30-39. *The cytoskeleton within cells and the universal patterns of design.*

■ **The Shifting Scaffolds of the Cell** New Scientist, 18 February 1989, pp. 44-47. *Microtubules in the cell are constantly moving.*

See pages 4-5 for details of how to access **Bio Links** from our web site: **www.thebiozone.com** From Bio Links, access sites under the topics:

GENERAL BIOLOGY ONLINE RESOURCES
• Biology I interactive animations • Instructional multimedia, University of Alberta • HowStuffWorks • Biointeractive ... *and others* > **Online Textbooks and Lecture Notes:** • S-Cool! A level biology revision guide Learn.co.uk ... *and others* > **Glossaries:** • Cellular biology: Glossary of terms • Kimball's biology glossary

CELL BIOLOGY AND BIOCHEMISTRY: • Cell and molecular biology online • Cell structure and function web links > **Microscopy:** • A guide to microscopy and microanalysis • Biological applications of electron and light microscopy • Histology • Microscopy UK • Scanning Electron Microscope ... *and others* > **Cell Structure and Transport:** • Animal cells • CELLS alive! • Cell breakage and fractionation - Part 1 • Nanoworld • Talksaver cell biology • The virtual cell • Techniques of cell fractionation

Presentation MEDIA to support this topic:

CELL BIO & BIOCHEM
• Cell Structure

The Cell Theory

The idea that all living things are composed of cells developed over many years and is strongly linked to the invention and refinement of the microscope. Early microscopes in the 1600's (such as Leeuwenhoek's below) opened up a whole new field of biology; the study of cell biology and microorganisms. The cell theory is a fundamental idea of biology.

Early Microscopes

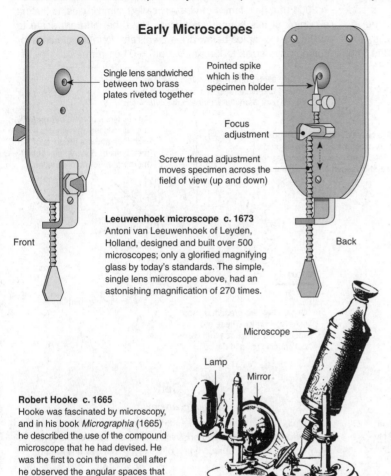

Single lens sandwiched between two brass plates riveted together

Pointed spike which is the specimen holder

Focus adjustment

Screw thread adjustment moves specimen across the field of view (up and down)

Front

Back

Leeuwenhoek microscope c. 1673
Antoni van Leeuwenhoek of Leyden, Holland, designed and built over 500 microscopes; only a glorified magnifying glass by today's standards. The simple, single lens microscope above, had an astonishing magnification of 270 times.

Microscope

Lamp

Mirror

Robert Hooke c. 1665
Hooke was fascinated by microscopy, and in his book *Micrographia* (1665) he described the use of the compound microscope that he had devised. He was the first to coin the name cell after he observed the angular spaces that he saw in a thin section of cork.

Milestones in Cell Biology

1500s	Convex lenses with a magnification greater than x5 became available.
Early 1600s	First compound microscopes used in Europe (used two convex lenses to make objects look larger). Suffered badly from colour distortion; an effect called 'spherical aberration'.
1632-1723	**Antoni van Leeuwenhoek** of Leyden, Holland, produced over 500 single lens microscopes. Discovered bacteria, human blood cells, spermatozoa, and protozoa. Friend of Robert Hooke of England.
1661	**Marcello Malpighi** used lenses to study insects. Discovered capillaries and may have described cells in writing of 'globules' and 'saccules'.
1662	**Robert Hooke** introduced the term 'cell' in describing the microscopic structure of cork. He believed that the cell walls were the important part of otherwise empty structures. Published *Micrographia* in 1665.
1672	**Nehemlah Grew** wrote the first of two well-illustrated books on the microscopic anatomy of plants.
1700s	Little serious work published.
1838-1839	Botanist **Matthias Schleiden** and zoologist **Theodor Schwann** proposed the *cell theory* for plants and animals: *plants and animals are composed of groups of cells and that the cell is the basic unit of living organisms.*
1855	**Rudolph Virchow** extended the cell theory by stating that: *new cells are formed only by the division of previously existing cells.*
1880	**August Weismann** added to Virchow's idea by pointing out that: *all the cells living today can trace their ancestry back to ancient times* (the link between cell theory and evolution).

The Cell Theory

The idea that cells are fundamental units of life is part of the cell theory. These ideas were formulated by a number of early biologists (see "Milestones in Cell Biology" on the right).

1. All living things are composed of cells and cell products.

2. New cells are formed only by the division of pre-existing cells.

3. The cell contains inherited information (genes) that are used as instructions for growth, functioning, and development.

4. The cell is the functioning unit of life; the chemical reactions of life take place within cells.

1. Briefly describe the impact the invention of microscopes has had on biology: _____

_____

_____

2. Before the development of the cell theory, it was commonly believed that living organisms could arise by spontaneous generation. Explain what this term means and why it has been discredited as a theory:

_____

_____

_____

Cell Structure

Code: A 2

Characteristics of Life

Living things share a suite of characteristics: movement, respiration, sensitivity, growth, reproduction, excretion, and nutrition. The cell is the site of life; it is the functioning unit structure from which living organisms are made. Viruses and cells are profoundly different (see the diagram below). Viruses are non-cellular, lack the complex structures found in cells, and show only some of the eight characteristics of living things. The traditional view of viruses is as a minimal particle, containing just enough genetic information to infect a host and highjack the host's machinery into replicating more viral particles. The identification in 2004 of a new family of viruses, called mimiviruses, is forcing a rethink of this conservative view. Note the different scale to which the examples below are drawn; refer to the scale bars for comparative sizes (1000 nm = 1 μm = 0.001 mm).

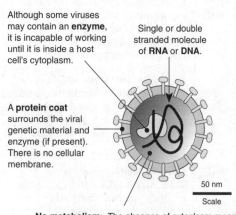

Although some viruses may contain an **enzyme**, it is incapable of working until it is inside a host cell's cytoplasm.

Single or double stranded molecule of **RNA** or **DNA**.

A **protein coat** surrounds the viral genetic material and enzyme (if present). There is no cellular membrane.

50 nm
Scale

No metabolism: The absence of cytoplasm means that a virus can not carry out any chemical reactions on its own; it is dependent upon parasitising a cell and using the cell's own machinery.

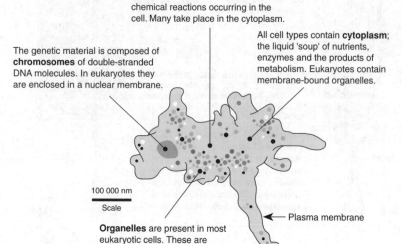

Metabolism: The total of all the chemical reactions occurring in the cell. Many take place in the cytoplasm.

The genetic material is composed of **chromosomes** of double-stranded DNA molecules. In eukaryotes they are enclosed in a nuclear membrane.

All cell types contain **cytoplasm**; the liquid 'soup' of nutrients, enzymes and the products of metabolism. Eukaryotes contain membrane-bound organelles.

100 000 nm
Scale

Plasma membrane

Organelles are present in most eukaryotic cells. These are specialised structures that carry out specific roles in the cell.

Virus
(e.g. HIV)

Viruses cannot become active outside a living host cell. They simply exist as inert virus particles called **virions**. Only when they invade a cell and take over the cell's metabolic machinery, can the virus carry out its 'living programme'.

Cell
(e.g. Amoeba)

Cells remain alive so long as their metabolic reactions in the cytoplasm are maintained. With a few rare exceptions (that involve freezing certain types of cells) if metabolism is halted, the cell dies.

1. Identify three features that all cells have in common: _____

    _____

2. Describe how cells differ from viruses in the following aspects:

    (a) Size: _____

    _____

    (b) Metabolism: _____

    _____

    (c) Organelles: _____

    _____

    (d) Genetic material: _____

    _____

    (e) Life cycle: _____

    _____

3. Viruses are not considered 'living' when outside a host cell. Give the general name for this state: _____

4. Explain why many biologists do not consider viruses to be living organisms: _____

    _____

Types of Living Things

Living things are called organisms and **cells** are the functioning unit structure from which organisms are made. Under the five kingdom system, cells can be divided into two basic kinds: the **prokaryotes**, which are simple cells without a distinct, membrane-bound nucleus, and the more complex **eukaryotes**. The eukaryotes can be further organised into broad groups according to their basic cell type: the protists, fungi, plants, and animals. Viruses are non-cellular and have no cellular machinery of their own. All cells must secure a source of energy if they are to survive and carry out metabolic processes. **Autotrophs** can meet their energy requirements using light or chemical energy from the physical environment. Other types of cell, called **heterotrophs**, obtain their energy from other living organisms or their dead remains.

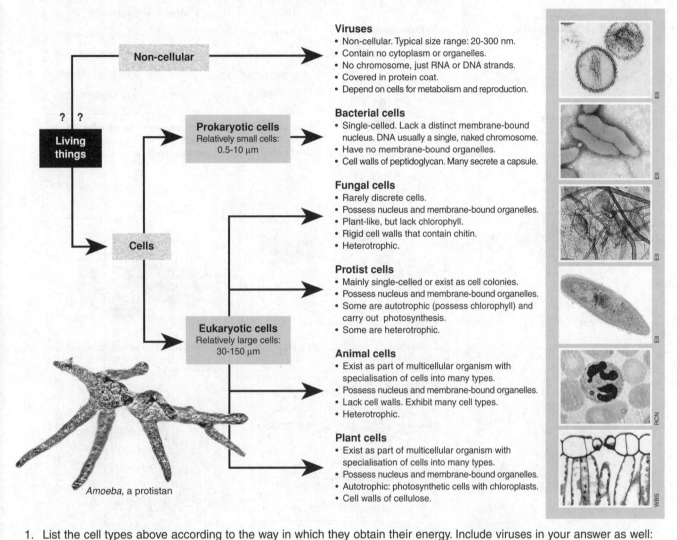

Non-cellular

? ?

Living things

Prokaryotic cells
Relatively small cells:
0.5-10 μm

Cells

Eukaryotic cells
Relatively large cells:
30-150 μm

Amoeba, a protistan

Viruses
- Non-cellular. Typical size range: 20-300 nm.
- Contain no cytoplasm or organelles.
- No chromosome, just RNA or DNA strands.
- Covered in protein coat.
- Depend on cells for metabolism and reproduction.

Bacterial cells
- Single-celled. Lack a distinct membrane-bound nucleus. DNA usually a single, naked chromosome.
- Have no membrane-bound organelles.
- Cell walls of peptidoglycan. Many secrete a capsule.

Fungal cells
- Rarely discrete cells.
- Possess nucleus and membrane-bound organelles.
- Plant-like, but lack chlorophyll.
- Rigid cell walls that contain chitin.
- Heterotrophic.

Protist cells
- Mainly single-celled or exist as cell colonies.
- Possess nucleus and membrane-bound organelles.
- Some are autotrophic (possess chlorophyll) and carry out photosynthesis.
- Some are heterotrophic.

Animal cells
- Exist as part of multicellular organism with specialisation of cells into many types.
- Possess nucleus and membrane-bound organelles.
- Lack cell walls. Exhibit many cell types.
- Heterotrophic.

Plant cells
- Exist as part of multicellular organism with specialisation of cells into many types.
- Possess nucleus and membrane-bound organelles.
- Autotrophic: photosynthetic cells with chloroplasts.
- Cell walls of cellulose.

1. List the cell types above according to the way in which they obtain their energy. Include viruses in your answer as well:

   (a) Autotrophic: _____

   (b) Heterotrophic: _____

2. Consult the diagram above and determine the two main features distinguishing **eukaryotic** cells from **prokaryotic** cells:

   (a) _____

   (b) _____

3. (a) Suggest why fungi were once classified as belonging to the plant kingdom: _____

   _____

   (b) Explain why, in terms of the distinguishing features of fungi, this classification was erroneous: _____

   _____

   _____

4. Suggest why the Protista have traditionally been a difficult group to classify: _____

   _____

Cell Structure

Code: A 1

Cell Sizes

Cells are extremely small and can only be seen properly when viewed through the magnifying lenses of a microscope. The diagrams below show a variety of cell types, together with a virus and a microscopic animal for comparison. For each of these images, note the scale and relate this to the type of microscopy used.

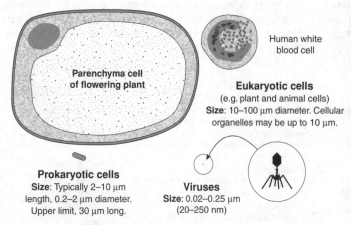

Parenchyma cell of flowering plant

Human white blood cell

Eukaryotic cells
(e.g. plant and animal cells)
Size: 10–100 μm diameter. Cellular organelles may be up to 10 μm.

Prokaryotic cells
Size: Typically 2–10 μm length, 0.2–2 μm diameter. Upper limit, 30 μm long.

Viruses
Size: 0.02–0.25 μm (20–250 nm)

Units of length (International System)

Unit	Metres	Equivalent
1 metre (m)	1 m	= 1000 millimetres
1 millimetre (mm)	10^{-3} m	= 1000 micrometres
1 micrometre (μm)	10^{-6} m	= 1000 nanometres
1 nanometre (nm)	10^{-9} m	= 1000 picometres

Micrometres are sometime referred to as **microns**. Smaller structures are usually measured in nanometres (nm) e.g. molecules (1 nm) and plasma membrane thickness (10 nm).

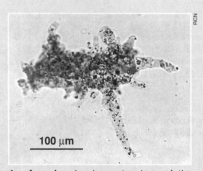

An **Amoeba** showing extensions of the cytoplasm called pseudopodia. This protoctist changes its shape, exploring its environment.

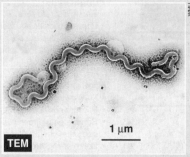

A long thin cell of the spirochete bacterium **Leptospira pomona**, which causes the disease leptospirosis.

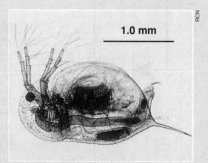

Daphnia showing its internal organs. These freshwater microcrustaceans are part of the zooplankton found in lakes and ponds.

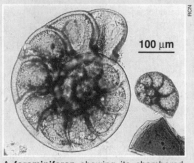

A **foraminiferan** showing its chambered, calcified shell. These single-celled protozoans are marine planktonic amoebae.

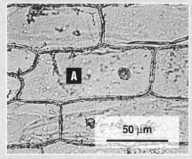

Epidermal cells (skin) from an onion bulb showing the nucleus, cell walls and cytoplasm. Organelles are not visible at this resolution.

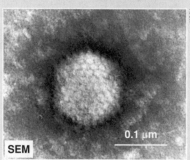

Papillomavirus (human wart virus) showing its polyhedral protein coat (20 triangular faces, 12 corners) made of ball-shaped structures.

1. Using the measurement scales provided on each of the photographs above, determine the longest dimension (length or diameter) of the cell/animal/virus in μm and mm (choose the cell marked **A** for epidermal cells):

(a) *Amoeba*: _____ μm _____ mm   (d) Epidermis: _____ μm _____ mm

(b) Foraminiferan: _____ μm _____ mm   (e) *Daphnia*: _____ μm _____ mm

(c) *Leptospira*: _____ μm _____ mm   (f) *Papillomavirus*: _____ μm _____ mm

2. List these six organisms in order of size, from the smallest to the largest: _____

3. Study the scale of your ruler and state which of these six organisms you would be able to see with your unaided eye:

4. Calculate the equivalent length in millimetres (mm) of the following measurements:

(a) 0.25 μm: _____   (b) 450 μm: _____   (c) 200 nm: _____

Cellular Environments

Cells must survive in a wide variety of environments (as illustrated below). Some provide conditions that are easy for cells to survive in, while others are so hostile that only cells with special adaptive features can survive. The environment that most closely resembles the inside of cells is sea water. This is hardly surprising as life almost certainly evolved in the oceans. Harsher environments such as freshwater lakes require cells to cope with the lack of dissolved salts. As multicellular plants and animals evolved, it became possible to shield the cells from the rigours of the outside environment within the surface layer of the body. Some local or regional environments may be altered by natural processes or human activity to create difficult conditions for cell survival. Pollutants from human industry and agriculture can produce waterways that are acidic, and soil that is contaminated with high levels of pesticides or heavy metals. Natural climate changes can result in hypersaline (high salt) lakes and soils.

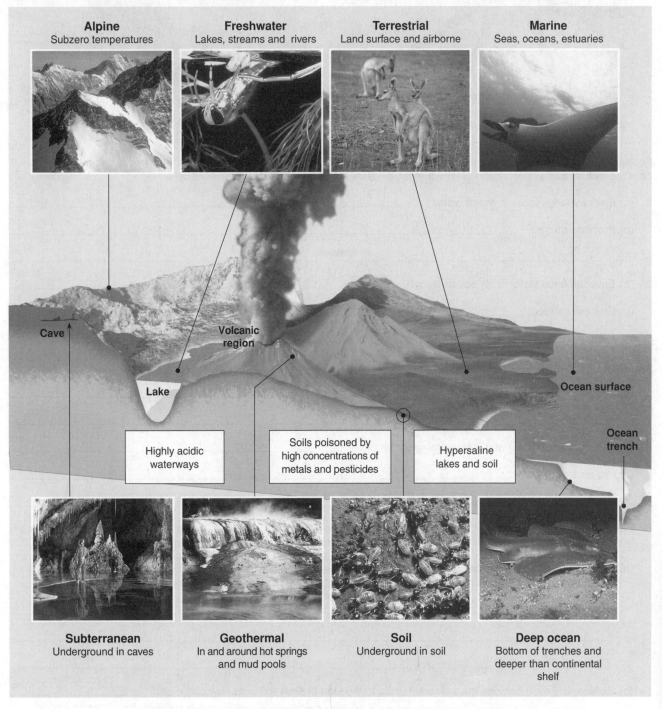

Alpine
Subzero temperatures

Freshwater
Lakes, streams and rivers

Terrestrial
Land surface and airborne

Marine
Seas, oceans, estuaries

Cave

Volcanic region

Lake

Ocean surface

Ocean trench

Highly acidic waterways

Soils poisoned by high concentrations of metals and pesticides

Hypersaline lakes and soil

Subterranean
Underground in caves

Geothermal
In and around hot springs and mud pools

Soil
Underground in soil

Deep ocean
Bottom of trenches and deeper than continental shelf

Cell Structure

1. Describe why the marine environment is the least stressful (relative to other environments) for cells to survive in:

_____

_____

_____

_____

_____

Code: RA 2

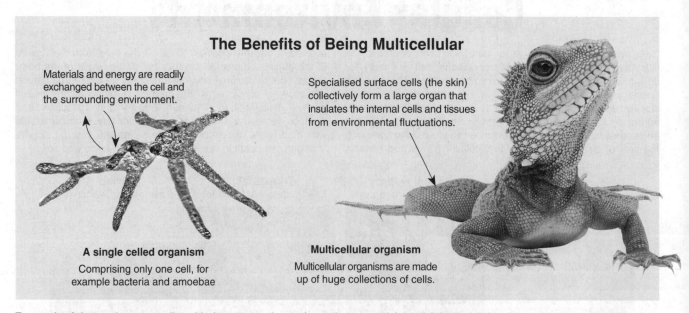

The Benefits of Being Multicellular

Materials and energy are readily exchanged between the cell and the surrounding environment.

Specialised surface cells (the skin) collectively form a large organ that insulates the internal cells and tissues from environmental fluctuations.

A single celled organism
Comprising only one cell, for example bacteria and amoebae

Multicellular organism
Multicellular organisms are made up of huge collections of cells.

For each of the environments listed below, name the main environmental (abiotic) factor(s) that may cause problems for cells, as well as a brief description of how that factor causes a problem for the survival of cells:

2. (a) Environmental factor in **fresh water:** _____

    (b) Problem caused: _____

_____

3. (a) Environmental factor in an **ocean trench:** _____

    (b) Problem caused: _____

_____

4. (a) Environmental factor in **hot springs:** _____

    (b) Problem caused: _____

_____

5. (a) Factor in **terrestrial** (land surface) environments: _____

    (b) Problem caused: _____

_____

6. Bacteria are single-celled organisms that are successful in a wide range of environments. Some of these environments are particularly hostile for other life forms and yet certain bacteria thrive in them.

    (a) Suggest a reason why bacteria are able to exploit hostile physical environments, taking into account how their cell structure and cell metabolism (chemistry of their cell) differs from that of plant and animal cells:

_____

_____

_____

    (b) Explain why even bacteria have physical limits to the kind of environments they can exploit: _____

_____

_____

7. Explain why multicellular organisms may have an advantage when living in some environments: _____

_____

_____

Optical Microscopes

The light microscope is one of the most important instruments used in biology practicals, and its correct use is a basic and essential skill of biology. High power light microscopes use a combination of lenses to magnify objects up to several hundred times. They are called **compound microscopes** because there are two or more separate lenses involved. A typical compound light microscope (bright field) is shown below (top photograph). The specimens viewed with these microscopes must be thin and mostly transparent. Light is focused up through the condenser and specimen; if the specimen is thick or opaque, little or no detail will be visible. The microscope below has two eyepieces (**binocular**), although monocular microscopes, with a mirror rather than an internal light source, may still be encountered. Dissecting microscopes (lower photograph) are a type of binocular microscope used for observations at low total magnification (x4 to x50), where a large working distance between objective lenses and stage is required. A dissecting microscope has two separate lens systems, one for each eye. Such microscopes produce a 3-D view of the specimen and are sometimes called stereo microscopes for this reason.

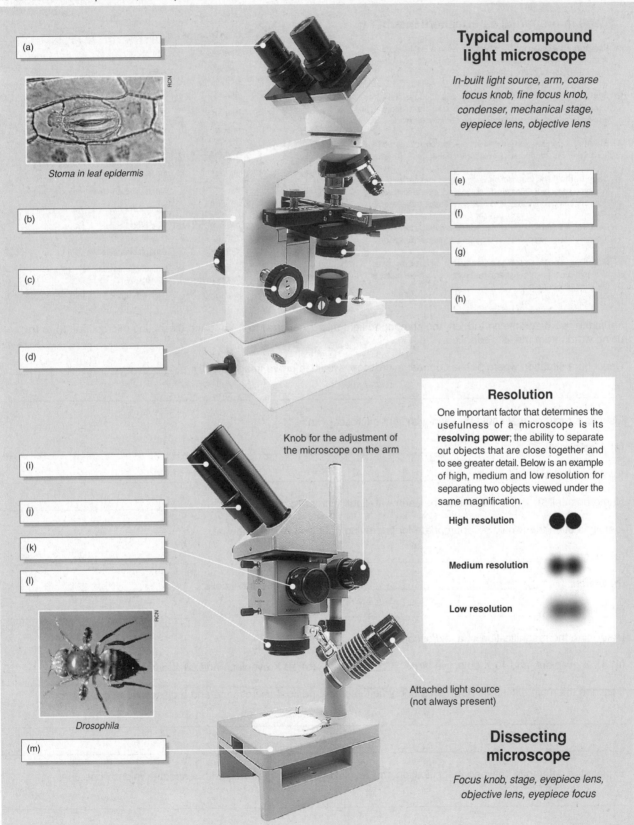

(a)

Stoma in leaf epidermis

(b)

(c)

(d)

Typical compound light microscope

In-built light source, arm, coarse focus knob, fine focus knob, condenser, mechanical stage, eyepiece lens, objective lens

(e)

(f)

(g)

(h)

Knob for the adjustment of the microscope on the arm

(i)

(j)

(k)

(l)

Drosophila

(m)

Attached light source (not always present)

Resolution

One important factor that determines the usefulness of a microscope is its **resolving power**; the ability to separate out objects that are close together and to see greater detail. Below is an example of high, medium and low resolution for separating two objects viewed under the same magnification.

High resolution

Medium resolution

Low resolution

Dissecting microscope

Focus knob, stage, eyepiece lens, objective lens, eyepiece focus

Cell Structure

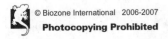
Code: RDA 2

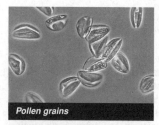

Pollen grains

Phase contrast illumination increases contrast of transparent specimens by producing interference effects.

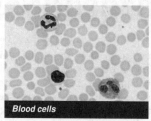

Blood cells

Leishman's stain is used to show red blood cells as red/pink, while staining the nucleus of white blood cells blue.

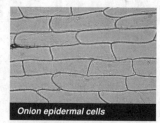

Onion epidermal cells

Standard bright field lighting shows cells with little detail; only cell walls, with the cell nuclei barely visible.

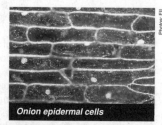

Onion epidermal cells

Dark field illumination is excellent for viewing near transparent specimens. The nucleus of each cell is visible.

Steps in preparing a permanent mount

1. **Fixation**: Preserves freshly killed tissues in a lifelike state by immersing them in a chemical (e.g. formalin) or applying heat (as in the case of microorganisms).

2. **Sectioning**: Cutting very thin sections; thin enough to let light through. May be embedded in wax or plastic and sliced with a microtome, or sectioned with a hand-held razor blade.

3. **Staining**: Dyes are applied that stain some structures while leaving others unaffected (see table on right).

4. **Dehydration**: The thin section is immersed in a series of increasing concentrations of ethanol to gradually remove water from the sample. This helps to make the tissue transparent.

5. **Clearing**: A liquid such as xylol is added to replace the ethanol (used above) and ensures the material remains transparent.

6. **Mounting**: The thin sections are mounted on a microscope slide in a medium (e.g. balsam) that excludes air and protects the sample indefinitely.

Stain	Final colour	Application
Temporary stains		
Iodine solution	blue-black	Starch
Aniline sulfate or Aniline hydrochloride	yellow	Lignin
Schultz's solution	blue	Starch
	blue or violet	Cellulose
	yellow	Protein, cutin, lignin, suberin
Permanent stains		
Methylene blue	blue	Nuclei
Safranin	red	Nuclei; suberin and lignin of plants
Aniline blue	blue	Fungal spores and hyphae
Leishman's stain	red-pink	Red blood cells
	blue	Nucleus of white blood cells
Eosin	pink/red	Cytoplasm/cellulose
Haematoxylin	blue	Nuclei of animal cells
(NOTE: mainly used as a counterstain for eosin)		
Feulgen's stain	red/purple	DNA (chromosomes in cell division)

1. Label the two diagrams on the left, the compound light microscope (a) to (h) and the dissecting microscope (i) to (m), using words from the lists supplied.

2. Describe a situation where phase contrast microscopy would improve image quality: _____

_____

3. List two structures that could be seen with light microscopy in:

   (a) A plant cell: _____

   (b) An animal cell: _____

4. Name one cell structure that cannot be seen with light microscopy: _____

5. Identify a stain that would be appropriate for improving definition of the following:

   (a) Blood cells: _____   (d) Fungal spores: _____

   (b) Starch: _____   (e) Nuclei of animal cells: _____

   (c) DNA: _____   (f) Cellulose: _____

6. Determine the magnification of a microscope using:

   (a) 15 X eyepiece and 40 X objective lens: _____   (b) 10 X eyepiece and 60 X objective lens: _____

7. Describe the main difference between a bright field, compound light microscope and a dissecting microscope:

_____

_____

8. Explain the difference between magnification and resolution (resolving power) with respect to microscope use:

_____

_____

Electron Microscopes

Electron microscopes (EMs) use a beam of electrons, instead of light, to produce an image. The higher resolution of EMs is due to the shorter wavelengths of electrons. There are two basic types of electron microscope: **scanning electron microscopes** (SEMs) and **transmission electron microscopes** (TEMs). In SEMs, the electrons are bounced off the surface of an object to produce detailed images of the external appearance. TEMs produce very clear images of specially prepared thin sections.

Transmission Electron Microscope (TEM)

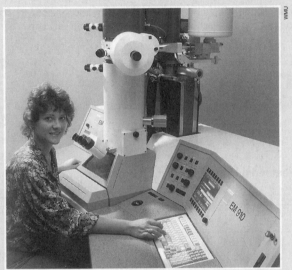

The transmission electron microscope is used to view extremely thin sections of material. Electrons pass through the specimen and are scattered. Magnetic lenses focus the image onto a fluorescent screen or photographic plate. The sections are so thin that they have to be prepared with a special machine, called an **ultramicrotome**, that can cut wafers to just 30 thousandths of a millimetre thick. It can magnify several hundred thousand times.

TEM

Electron gun

Electron beam

Electromagnetic condenser lens

Specimen

Vacuum pump

Electromagnetic objective lens

Electromagnetic projector lens

Eyepiece

Fluorescent screen or photographic plate

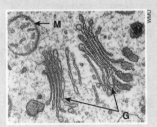

TEM photo showing the Golgi (**G**) and a mitochondrion (**M**).

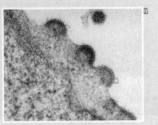

Three HIV viruses budding out of a human lymphocyte (TEM).

Scanning Electron Microscope (SEM)

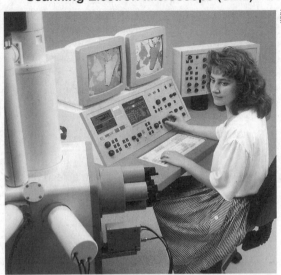

The scanning electron microscope scans a sample with a beam of primary electrons that knock electrons from its surface. These secondary electrons are picked up by a collector, amplified, and transmitted onto a viewing screen or photographic plate, producing a superb 3-D image. A microscope of this power can easily obtain clear pictures of organisms as small as bacteria and viruses. The image produced is of the outside surface only.

SEM

Electron gun

Primary electron beam

Electromagnetic lenses

Vacuum pump

Electron collector

Amplifier

Viewing screen

Specimen   Secondary electrons

SEM photo of stoma and epidermal cells on the upper surface of a leaf.

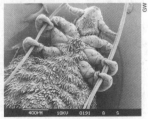

Image of hair louse clinging to two hairs on a Hooker's sealion (SEM).

Cell Structure

Code: RA 2

	Light Microscope	Transmission Electron Microscope (TEM)	Scanning Electron Microscope (SEM)
Radiation source:	light	electrons	electrons
Wavelength:	400-700 nm	0.005 nm	0.005 nm
Lenses:	glass	electromagnetic	electromagnetic
Specimen:	living or non-living supported on glass slide	non-living supported on a small copper grid in a vacuum	non-living supported on a metal disc in a vacuum
Maximum resolution:	200 nm	1 nm	10 nm
Maximum magnification:	1500 x	250 000 x	100 000 x
Stains:	coloured dyes	impregnated with heavy metals	coated with carbon or gold
Type of image:	coloured	monochrome (black & white)	monochrome (black & white)

1. Explain why electron microscopes are able to resolve much greater detail than a light microscope:

   _____

   _____

   _____

2. Describe two typical applications for each of the following types of microscope:

   (a) Transmission electron microscope (TEM): _____

   _____

   (b) Scanning electron microscope (SEM): _____

   _____

   (c) Bright field, compound light microscope (thin section): _____

   _____

   (d) Dissecting microscope: _____

   _____

3. Identify which type of electron microscope (SEM or TEM) or optical microscope (bright field, compound light microscope or dissecting microscope) was used to produce each of the images in the photos below (A-H):

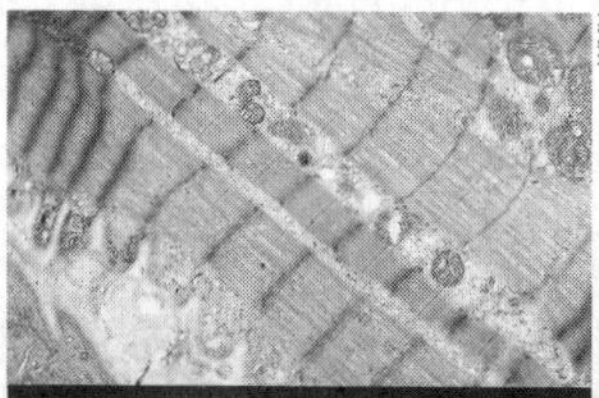

Cardiac muscle

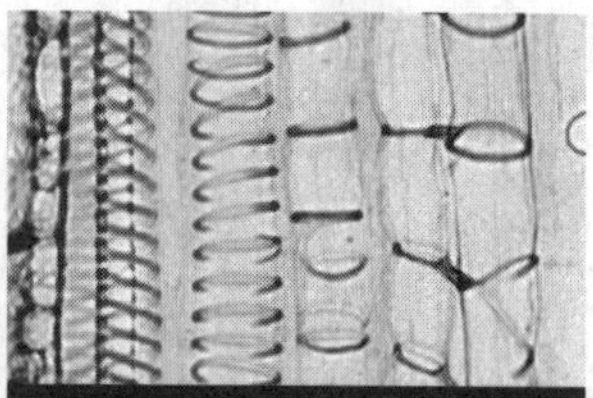

Plant vascular tissue

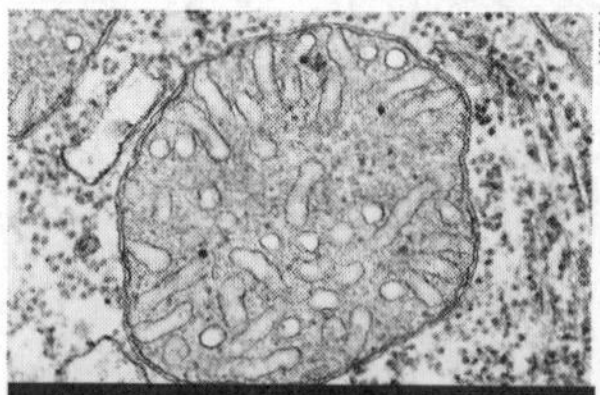

Mitochondrion

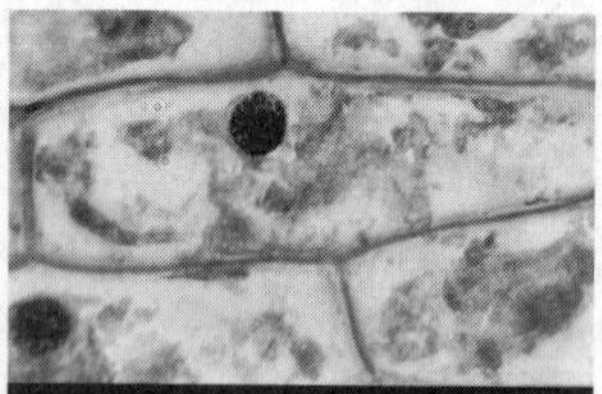

Plant epidermal cells

A _____   B _____   C _____   D _____

Head louse

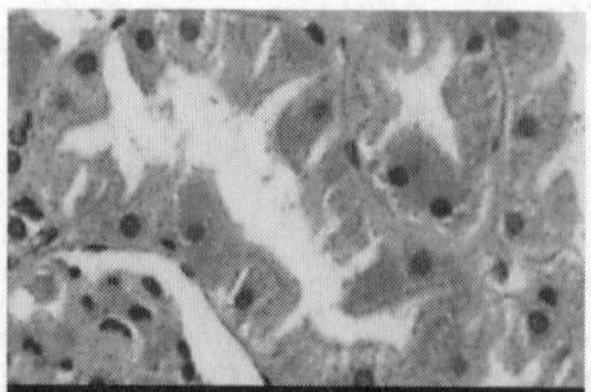

Kidney cells

Alderfly larva

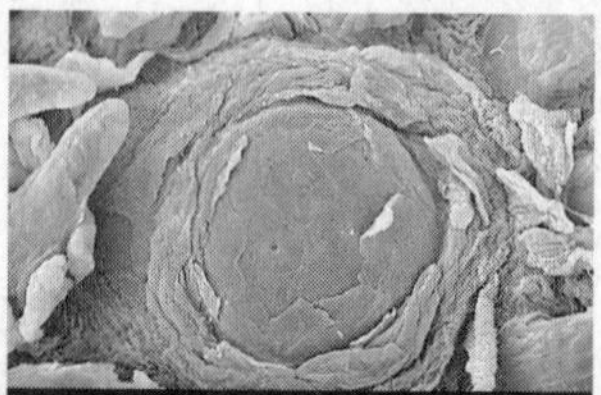

Tongue papilla

E _____   F _____   G _____   H _____

Plant Cells

Plant cells are enclosed in a cellulose cell wall. The cell wall protects the cell, maintains its shape, and prevents excessive water uptake. It does not interfere with the passage of materials into and out of the cell. The diagram below shows the structure and function of a typical plant cell and its organelles. Also see the following page where further information is provided on the organelles listed here but not described.

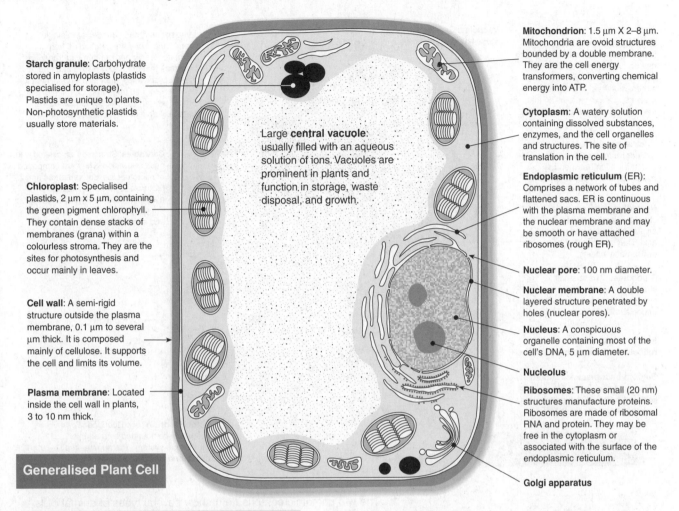

Starch granule: Carbohydrate stored in amyloplasts (plastids specialised for storage). Plastids are unique to plants. Non-photosynthetic plastids usually store materials.

Chloroplast: Specialised plastids, 2 µm x 5 µm, containing the green pigment chlorophyll. They contain dense stacks of membranes (grana) within a colourless stroma. They are the sites for photosynthesis and occur mainly in leaves.

Cell wall: A semi-rigid structure outside the plasma membrane, 0.1 µm to several µm thick. It is composed mainly of cellulose. It supports the cell and limits its volume.

Plasma membrane: Located inside the cell wall in plants, 3 to 10 nm thick.

Large **central vacuole**: usually filled with an aqueous solution of ions. Vacuoles are prominent in plants and function in storage, waste disposal, and growth.

Mitochondrion: 1.5 µm X 2–8 µm. Mitochondria are ovoid structures bounded by a double membrane. They are the cell energy transformers, converting chemical energy into ATP.

Cytoplasm: A watery solution containing dissolved substances, enzymes, and the cell organelles and structures. The site of translation in the cell.

Endoplasmic reticulum (ER): Comprises a network of tubes and flattened sacs. ER is continuous with the plasma membrane and the nuclear membrane and may be smooth or have attached ribosomes (rough ER).

Nuclear pore: 100 nm diameter.

Nuclear membrane: A double layered structure penetrated by holes (nuclear pores).

Nucleus: A conspicuous organelle containing most of the cell's DNA, 5 µm diameter.

Nucleolus

Ribosomes: These small (20 nm) structures manufacture proteins. Ribosomes are made of ribosomal RNA and protein. They may be free in the cytoplasm or associated with the surface of the endoplasmic reticulum.

Golgi apparatus

Generalised Plant Cell

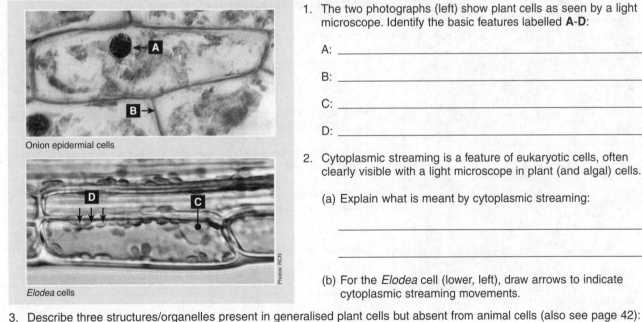

Onion epidermial cells

Elodea cells

1. The two photographs (left) show plant cells as seen by a light microscope. Identify the basic features labelled **A-D**:

A: _____

B: _____

C: _____

D: _____

2. Cytoplasmic streaming is a feature of eukaryotic cells, often clearly visible with a light microscope in plant (and algal) cells.

(a) Explain what is meant by cytoplasmic streaming:

_____

_____

(b) For the *Elodea* cell (lower, left), draw arrows to indicate cytoplasmic streaming movements.

3. Describe three structures/organelles present in generalised plant cells but absent from animal cells (also see page 42):

(a) _____

(b) _____

(c) _____

Cell Structure

Code: RA 2

Animal Cells

Animal cells, unlike plant cells, do not have a regular shape. In fact, some animal cells (such as phagocytes) are able to alter their shape for various purposes (e.g. engulfment of foreign material). The diagram below shows the structure and function of a typical animal cell and its organelles. Note the differences between this cell and the generalised plant cell. Also see the previous page where further information is provided on the organelles listed here but not described.

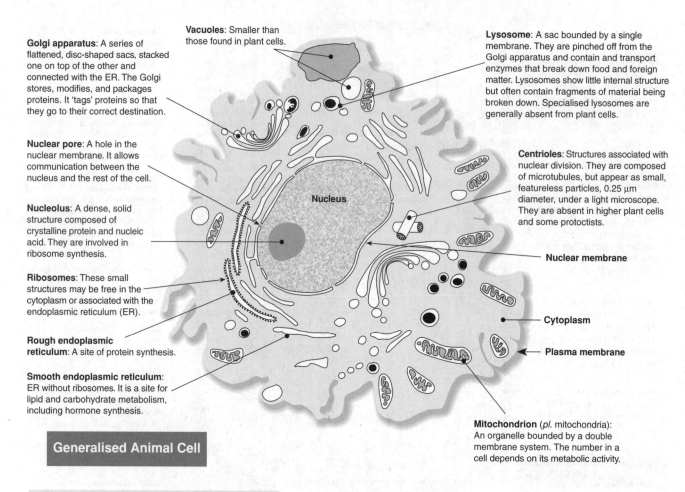

Golgi apparatus: A series of flattened, disc-shaped sacs, stacked one on top of the other and connected with the ER. The Golgi stores, modifies, and packages proteins. It 'tags' proteins so that they go to their correct destination.

Nuclear pore: A hole in the nuclear membrane. It allows communication between the nucleus and the rest of the cell.

Nucleolus: A dense, solid structure composed of crystalline protein and nucleic acid. They are involved in ribosome synthesis.

Ribosomes: These small structures may be free in the cytoplasm or associated with the endoplasmic reticulum (ER).

Rough endoplasmic reticulum: A site of protein synthesis.

Smooth endoplasmic reticulum: ER without ribosomes. It is a site for lipid and carbohydrate metabolism, including hormone synthesis.

Vacuoles: Smaller than those found in plant cells.

Nucleus

Lysosome: A sac bounded by a single membrane. They are pinched off from the Golgi apparatus and contain and transport enzymes that break down food and foreign matter. Lysosomes show little internal structure but often contain fragments of material being broken down. Specialised lysosomes are generally absent from plant cells.

Centrioles: Structures associated with nuclear division. They are composed of microtubules, but appear as small, featureless particles, 0.25 µm diameter, under a light microscope. They are absent in higher plant cells and some protoctists.

Nuclear membrane

Cytoplasm

Plasma membrane

Mitochondrion (*pl*. mitochondria): An organelle bounded by a double membrane system. The number in a cell depends on its metabolic activity.

Generalised Animal Cell

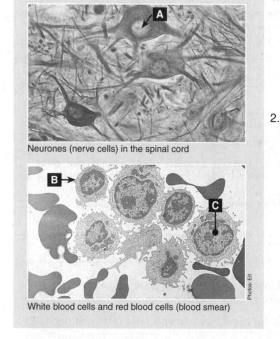

Neurones (nerve cells) in the spinal cord

White blood cells and red blood cells (blood smear)

Photos: Elf

1. The two photomicrographs (left) show several types of animal cells. Identify the features indicated by the letters **A-C**:

   A: _____

   B: _____

   C: _____

2. White blood cells are mobile, phagocytic cells, whereas red blood cells are smaller than white blood cells and, in humans, lack a nucleus.

   (a) In the photomicrograph (below, left), circle a white blood cell and a red blood cell:

   (b) With respect to the features that you can see, explain how you made your decision.

   _____

   _____

   _____

   _____

3. Name and describe one structure or organelle present in generalised animal cells but absent from plant cells:

_____

_____

Bacterial Cells

Bacterial (prokaryotic) cells are much smaller and simpler than the cells of eukaryotes. They lack many eukaryotic features (e.g. a distinct nucleus and membrane-bound cellular organelles). The bacterial cell wall is an important feature. It is a complex, multi-layered structure and often has a role in virulence. These pages illustrate some features of bacterial structure and diversity.

Structure of a Generalised Bacterial Cell

Plasmids: Small, circular DNA molecules (accessory chromosomes) which can reproduce independently of the main chromosome. They can move between cells, and even between species, by **conjugation**. This property accounts for the transmission of antibiotic resistance between bacteria. Plasmids are also used as vectors in recombinant DNA technology.

Single, circular main chromosome: Makes them haploid for most genes. It is possible for some genes to be found on both the plasmid and chromosome and there may be several copies of a gene on a group of plasmids.

The cell lacks a nuclear membrane, so there is no distinct nucleus and the chromosomes are in direct contact with the cytoplasm. It is possible for free ribosomes to attach to mRNA while the mRNA is still in the process of being transcribed from the DNA.

Fimbriae: Hairlike structures that are shorter, straighter, and thinner than flagella. They are used for attachment, not movement. Pili are similar to fimbriae, but are longer and less numerous. They are involved in bacterial conjugation (below) and as phage receptors (opposite).

1 μm

Cytoplasm

Cell surface membrane: Similar in composition to eukaryotic membranes, although less rigid.

Glycocalyx. A viscous, gelatinous layer outside the cell wall. It is composed of polysaccharide and/or polypeptide. If it is firmly attached to the wall, it is called a **capsule**. If loosely attached, it is called a **slime layer**. Capsules may contribute to virulence in pathogenic species, e.g. by protecting the bacteria from the host's immune attack. In some species, the glycocalyx allows attachment to substrates.

Cell wall. A complex, semi-rigid structure that gives the cell shape, prevents rupture, and serves as an anchorage point for flagella. The cell wall is composed of a macromolecule called **peptidoglycan**; repeating disaccharides attached by polypeptides to form a lattice. The wall also contains varying amounts of lipopolysaccharides and lipoproteins. The amount of peptidoglycan present in the wall forms the basis of the diagnostic **gram stain**. In many species, the cell wall contributes to their virulence (disease-causing ability).

Flagellum (pl. flagella). Some bacteria have long, filamentous appendages, called flagella, that are used for locomotion. There may be a single polar flagellum (monotrichous), one or more flagella at each end of the cell, or the flagella may be distributed over the entire cell (peritrichous).

Bacterial cell shapes

Most bacterial cells range between 0.20-2.0 μm in diameter and 2-10 μm length. Although they are a very diverse group, much of this diversity is in their metabolism. In terms of gross morphology, there are only a few basic shapes found (illustrated below). The way in which members of each group aggregate after division is often characteristic and is helpful in identifying certain species.

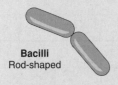

Bacilli
Rod-shaped

Bacilli: Rod-shaped bacteria that divide only across their short axis. Most occur as single rods, although pairs and chains are also found. The term bacillus can refer (as here) to shape. It may also denote a genus.

Cocci
Ball-shaped

Cocci: usually round, but sometimes oval or elongated. When they divide, the cells stay attached to each other and remain in aggregates e.g. pairs (diplococci) or clusters (staphylococci), that are usually a feature of the genus.

Spirilla
Spiral-shaped

Spirilla and vibrio: Bacteria with one or more twists. Spirilla bacteria have a helical (corkscrew) shape which may be rigid or flexible (as in spirochetes). Bacteria that look like curved rods (comma shaped) are called vibrios.

Bacterial conjugation

The two bacteria below are involved in conjugation: a one-way exchange of genetic information from a donor cell to a recipient cell. The plasmid, which must be of the 'conjugative' type, passes through a tube called a **sex pilus** to the other cell. Which is donor and which is recipient appears to be genetically determined. Conjugation should not be confused with sexual reproduction, as it does not involve the fusion of gametes or formation of a zygote.

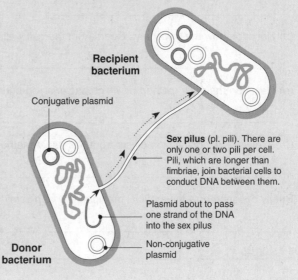

Recipient bacterium

Conjugative plasmid

Sex pilus (pl. pili). There are only one or two pili per cell. Pili, which are longer than fimbriae, join bacterial cells to conduct DNA between them.

Plasmid about to pass one strand of the DNA into the sex pilus

Non-conjugative plasmid

Donor bacterium

Cell Structure

Code: RA 2

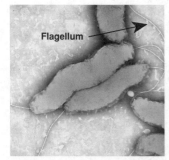

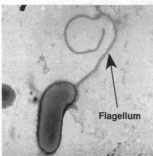

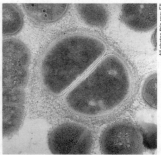

Campylobacter jejuni, a spiral bacterium responsible for foodborne intestinal disease. Note the single flagellum at each end (amphitrichous arrangement).

Helicobacter pylori, a comma-shaped vibrio bacterium that causes stomach ulcers in humans. This bacterium moves by means of multiple polar flagella.

A species of *Spirillum*, a spiral shaped bacterium with a tuft of polar flagella. Most of the species in this genus are harmless aquatic organisms.

Bacteria usually divide by binary fission. During this process, DNA is copied and the cell splits into two cells, as in these gram positive cocci.

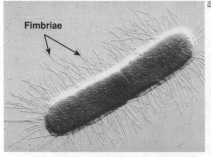

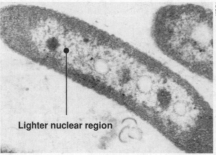

Escherichia coli, a common gut bacterium with **peritrichous** (around the entire cell) **fimbriae**. *E. coli* is a gram negative rod; it does not take up the gram stain but can be counter stained with safranin.

TEM showing *Enterobacter* bacteria, which belong to the family of gut bacteria commonly known as enterics. They are widely distributed in water, sewage, and soil. The family includes motile and non-motile species.

SEM of endospores of ***Bacillus anthracis*** bacteria, which cause the disease anthrax. These heat-resistant spores remain viable for many years and enable the bacteria to survive in a dormant state.

1. Describe three features distinguishing prokaryotic cells from eukaryotic cells:

   (a) _____

   (b) _____

   (c) _____

2. (a) Describe the function of flagella in bacteria: _____

   _____

   (b) Explain how fimbriae differ structurally and functionally from flagella: _____

   _____

   _____

3. (a) Describe the location and general composition of the bacterial cell wall: _____

   _____

   _____

   (b) Describe how the glycocalyx differs from the cell wall: _____

   _____

4. (a) Describe the main method by which bacteria reproduce: _____

   _____

   (b) Explain how conjugation differs from this usual method: _____

   _____

5. Briefly describe how the artificial manipulation of plasmids has been used for technological applications:

   _____

   _____

   _____

Fungal Cells

The fungi are a large, successful group of eukaryotes that includes the yeasts, moulds, and fleshy fungi. The study of fungi is called **mycology**. All fungi are chemoheterotrophs: they lack chlorophyll and require organic compounds for a source of energy and carbon. Most fungi are also **saprophytic**, feeding on dead material, although some are parasitic or mutualistic. Fungal nutrition is absorptive and digestion is extracellular and takes place outside the fungal body. Of more than 100 000 fungal species, only about 100 are pathogenic to humans or other animals. However, many are plant pathogens and virtually every economically important plant species is attacked by one or more fungi. Note that the **lichens** have been reclassified into the fungal kingdom. They are dual organisms, formed by a mutualistic association between a green alga or a cyanobacterium, and a fungus (usually an ascomycete). Features of two fungal groups: yeasts and moulds are described below.

Single Celled Fungi: Yeasts

Yeasts are nonfilamentous, unicellular fungi that are typically spherical or oval shaped. Yeasts reproduce asexually by fission or budding. They are facultative anaerobes, a property that is exploited in the brewing, wine making, and bread making industries.

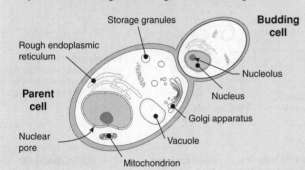

Filamentous Fungi: Moulds

Moulds are multicellular, filamentous fungi often divided by septa into uni-nucleate, cell-like units. When conditions are favourable, hyphae grow to form a filamentous mass called a **mycelium.**

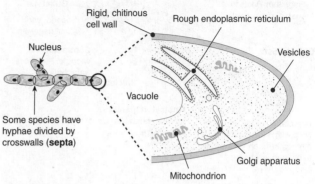

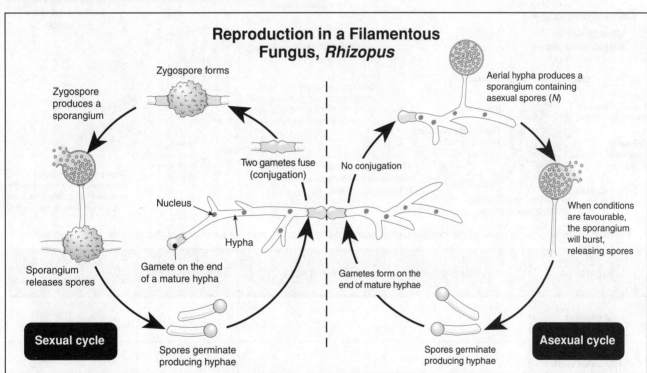

Reproduction in a Filamentous Fungus, *Rhizopus*

Zygospore forms

Zygospore produces a sporangium

Two gametes fuse (conjugation)

No conjugation

Aerial hypha produces a sporangium containing asexual spores (*N*)

When conditions are favourable, the sporangium will burst, releasing spores

Sporangium releases spores

Nucleus

Hypha

Gamete on the end of a mature hypha

Gametes form on the end of mature hyphae

Sexual cycle

Spores germinate producing hyphae

Spores germinate producing hyphae

Asexual cycle

1. List three distinguishing features of fungi: _____

_____

2. Outline the key differences in the reproductive strategies of yeasts and moulds: _____

_____

_____

3. Identify two commonly exploited fungal species and state how they are used:

   (a) _____

   (b) _____

Cell Structure

Code: RA 1

Unicellular Eukaryotes

Unicellular (single-celled) **eukaryotes** comprise the majority of the diverse kingdom, Protista. They are found almost anywhere there is water, including within larger organisms (as parasites or symbionts). The protists are a very diverse group, exhibiting some features typical of generalised eukaryotic cells, as well as specialised features, which may be specific to one genus. Note that even within the genera below there is considerable variation in size and appearance. *Amoeba* and *Paramecium* are both **heterotrophic**, ingesting food, which accumulates inside a **vacuole**. *Euglena* and *Chlamydomonas* are autotrophic algae, although *Euglena* is heterotrophic when deprived of light. Other protists include the marine foraminiferans and radiolarians, specialised intracellular parasites such as *Plasmodium*, and zooflagellates such as the parasites *Trypanosoma* and *Giardia*.

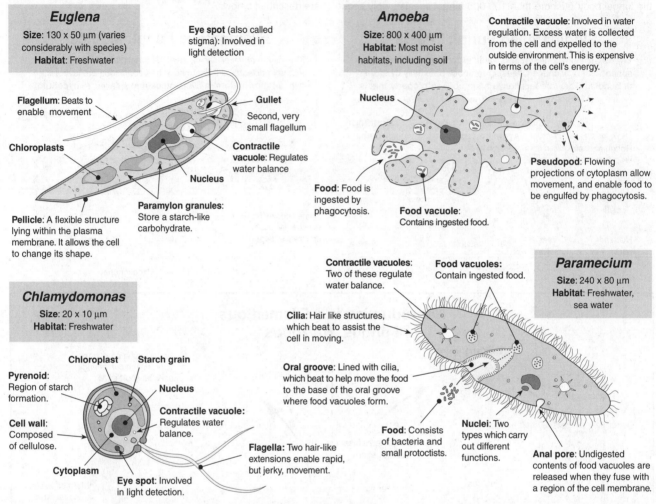

Euglena
Size: 130 x 50 μm (varies considerably with species)
Habitat: Freshwater

Eye spot (also called stigma): Involved in light detection

Flagellum: Beats to enable movement

Gullet
Second, very small flagellum

Chloroplasts

Contractile vacuole: Regulates water balance

Nucleus

Paramylon granules: Store a starch-like carbohydrate.

Pellicle: A flexible structure lying within the plasma membrane. It allows the cell to change its shape.

Amoeba
Size: 800 x 400 μm
Habitat: Most moist habitats, including soil

Contractile vacuole: Involved in water regulation. Excess water is collected from the cell and expelled to the outside environment. This is expensive in terms of the cell's energy.

Nucleus

Pseudopod: Flowing projections of cytoplasm allow movement, and enable food to be engulfed by phagocytosis.

Food: Food is ingested by phagocytosis.

Food vacuole: Contains ingested food.

Chlamydomonas
Size: 20 x 10 μm
Habitat: Freshwater

Chloroplast   **Starch grain**

Pyrenoid: Region of starch formation.

Nucleus

Cell wall: Composed of cellulose.

Contractile vacuole: Regulates water balance.

Cytoplasm

Eye spot: Involved in light detection.

Flagella: Two hair-like extensions enable rapid, but jerky, movement.

Contractile vacuoles: Two of these regulate water balance.

Food vacuoles: Contain ingested food.

Paramecium
Size: 240 x 80 μm
Habitat: Freshwater, sea water

Cilia: Hair like structures, which beat to assist the cell in moving.

Oral groove: Lined with cilia, which beat to help move the food to the base of the oral groove where food vacuoles form.

Food: Consists of bacteria and small protoctists.

Nuclei: Two types which carry out different functions.

Anal pore: Undigested contents of food vacuoles are released when they fuse with a region of the cell membrane.

1. Fill in the table below to summarise differences in some of the features and life functions of the protists shown above:

Organism	Nutrition	Movement	Osmoregulation	Eye spot present / absent	Cell wall present / absent
Amoeba					
Paramecium					
Euglena					
Chlamydomonas					

2. List the four organisms shown above in order of size (largest first): _____

_____

3. Suggest why an autotroph would have an eye spot: _____

_____

Code: A 1

Types of Cells

Cells come in a wide range of types and forms. The diagram below shows a selection of cell types from the five kingdoms. The variety that results from specialisation of undifferentiated cells is enormous. In the following exercise, identify which of the cell types belongs to each of the kingdoms and list the major distinguishing characteristics of their cells.

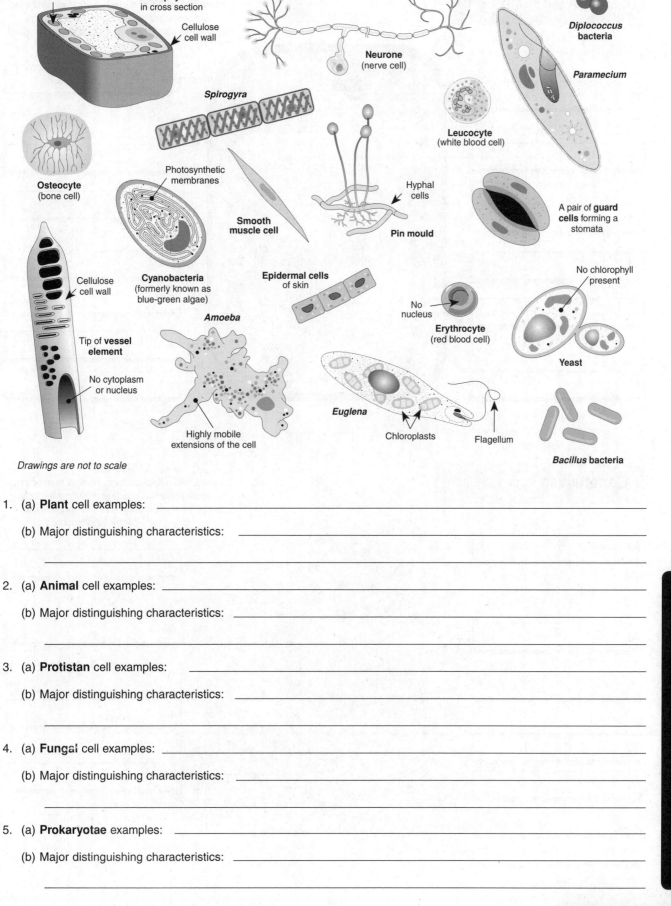

Drawings are not to scale

1. (a) **Plant** cell examples: _____

   (b) Major distinguishing characteristics: _____

   _____

2. (a) **Animal** cell examples: _____

   (b) Major distinguishing characteristics: _____

   _____

3. (a) **Protistan** cell examples: _____

   (b) Major distinguishing characteristics: _____

   _____

4. (a) **Fungal** cell examples: _____

   (b) Major distinguishing characteristics: _____

   _____

5. (a) **Prokaryotae** examples: _____

   (b) Major distinguishing characteristics: _____

Cell Structure

Code: RA 1

Review of Eukaryotic Cells

The diagrams below show the organelles and structures that are associated with plant and animal cells. From the word lists, revise previous material and use other references to identify and label the organelles depicted in the diagrams of the cells below.

Generalised Plant Cell

Vacuole, mitochondrion, cell wall, plasma membrane, nucleus, nucleolus, nuclear membrane, Golgi apparatus, endoplasmic reticulum, cytoplasm, starch granule, ribosomes, chloroplast

(a)

(b)

(c)

(d)

(e)

(f)

(g)

(h)

(i)

(j)

(k)

(l)

(m)

Generalised Animal Cell

WORD LIST
Lysosome, mitochondrion, plasma membrane, nucleus, nucleolus, nuclear membrane, nuclear pore, Golgi apparatus, endoplasmic reticulum, cytoplasm, centriole, ribosomes

(a)

(b)

(c)

(d)

(e)

(f)

(g)

(h)

(i)

(j)

(k)

(l)

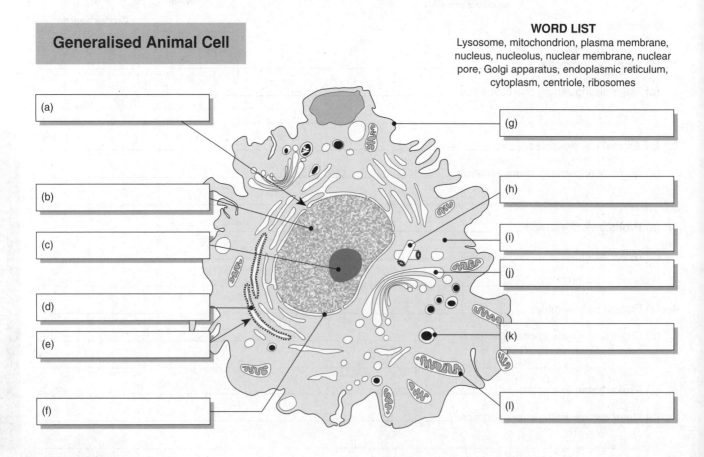

Code: R 1

Cell Structures and Organelles

The table below, and the following page, provides a format to summarise information about structures and organelles of typical eukaryotic cells. Complete the table using the list provided and by referring to a textbook and to other pages in this topic. Fill in the final three columns by writing either 'YES' or 'NO'. The first cell component has been completed for you as a guide and the log scale of measurements (top of next page) illustrates the relative sizes of some cellular structures. **List of structures and organelles**: cell wall, mitochondrion, chloroplast, centrioles, ribosome, endoplasmic reticulum, Golgi apparatus.

Cell Component	Details	Present in		Visible under light microscope
		Plant cells	Animal cells	
(a) 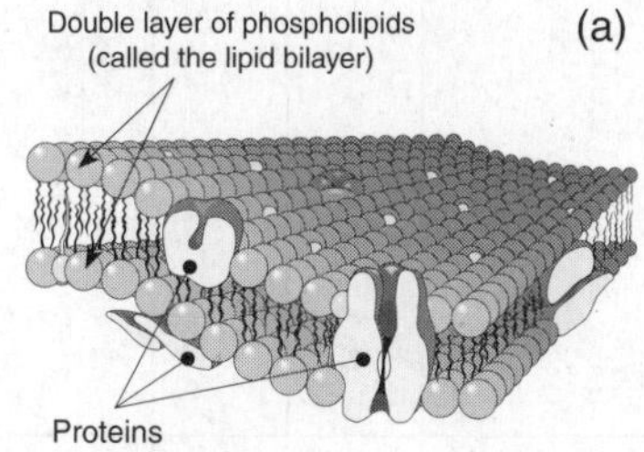 Double layer of phospholipids (called the lipid bilayer) Proteins	Name: Plasma (cell surface) membrane Location: Surrounding the cell Function: Gives the cell shape and protection. It also regulates the movement of substances into and out of the cell.	YES	YES	YES (but not at the level of detail shown in the diagram)
(b) 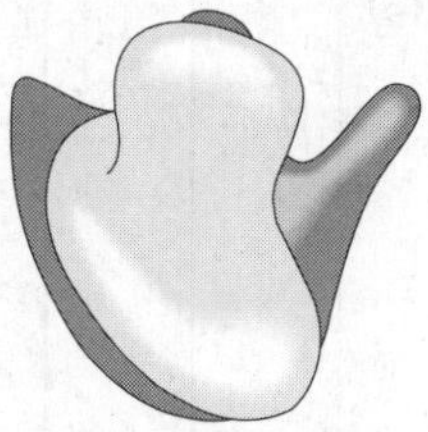	Name: Location: Function:			
(c) 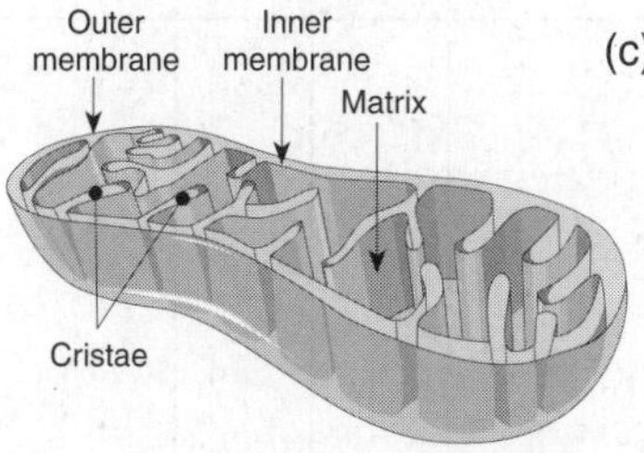 Outer membrane Inner membrane Matrix Cristae	Name: Location: Function:			
(d) 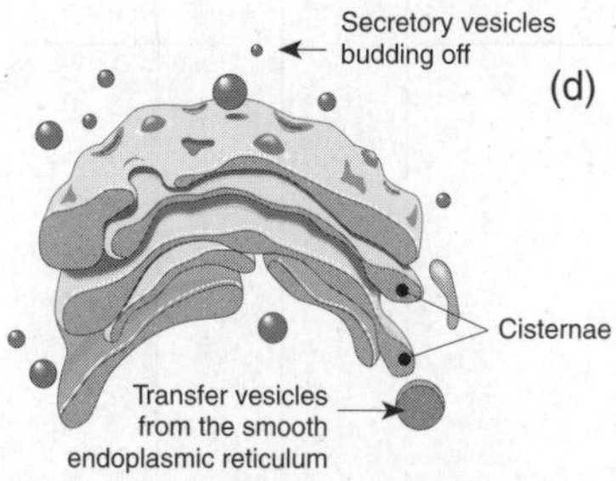 Secretory vesicles budding off Cisternae Transfer vesicles from the smooth endoplasmic reticulum	Name: Location: Function:			
(e) 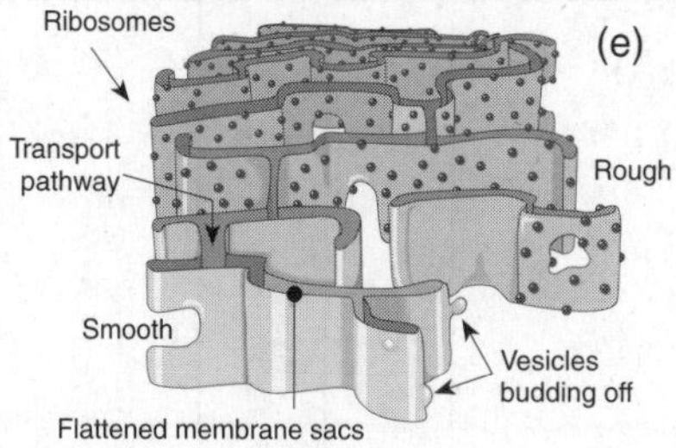 Ribosomes Transport pathway Rough Smooth Vesicles budding off Flattened membrane sacs	Name: Location: Function:			
(f) 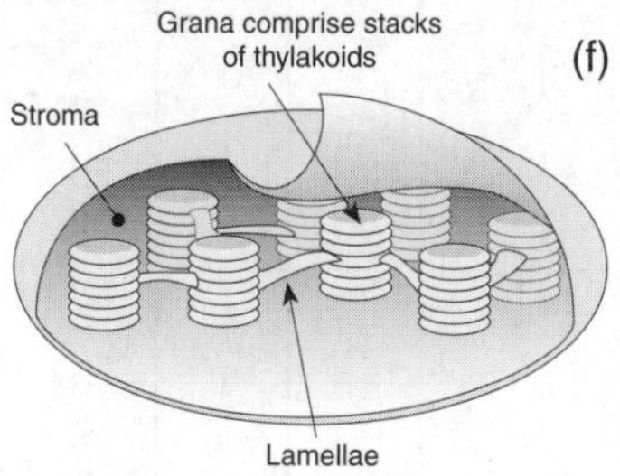 Grana comprise stacks of thylakoids Stroma Lamellae	Name: Location: Function:			

Cell Structure

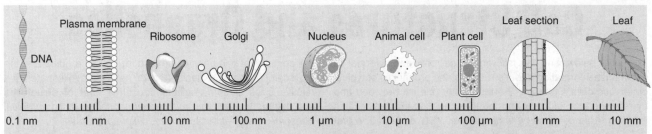

DNA | Plasma membrane | Ribosome | Golgi | Nucleus | Animal cell | Plant cell | Leaf section | Leaf

0.1 nm   1 nm   10 nm   100 nm   1 µm   10 µm   100 µm   1 mm   10 mm

Cell Component	Details	Present in		Visible under light microscope
		Plant cells	Animal cells	
(g) Microtubules	Name: Location: Function:			
(h) Two central, single microtubules — 9 doublets of microtubules in an outer ring — Extension of plasma membrane surrounding a core of microtubules in a 9+2 pattern — Basal body anchors the cilium	Name: Cilia and flagella (some eukaryotic cells) Location: Function:			
(i) Cross-layering of cellulose	Name: Location: Function:			
(j) Lysosome	Name: Lysosome Location: Function:			
(k) Food Vacuole — Phagocytosis	Name: Vacuole (a food vacuole is shown) Location: Function:			
(l) Nuclear membrane — Nuclear pores — Nucleolus — Genetic material	Name: Nucleus Location: Function:			

Interpreting Electron Micrographs

The photographs below were taken using a transmission electron microscope (TEM). They show some of the cell organelles in great detail. Remember that these photos are showing only **parts of cells, not whole cells**. Some of the photographs show more than one type of organelle. The questions refer to the main organelle in the centre of the photo.

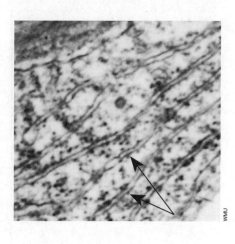

1. (a) Name this organelle (arrowed): _____

   (b) State which kind of cell(s) this organelle would be found in:

   _____

   (c) Describe the function of this organelle: _____

   _____

   _____

   (d) Label two structures that can be seen inside this organelle.

2. (a) Name this organelle (arrowed): _____

   (b) State which kind of cell(s) this organelle would be found in:

   _____

   (c) Describe the function of this organelle: _____

   _____

   _____

   _____

   _____

3. (a) Name the large, circular organelle: _____

   (b) State which kind of cell(s) this organelle would be found in:

   _____

   (c) Describe the function of this organelle: _____

   _____

   _____

   (d) Label two regions that can be seen inside this organelle.

4. (a) Name and label the ribbon-like organelle in this photograph (arrowed):

   _____

   (b) State which kind of cell(s) this organelle is found in:

   _____

   (c) Describe the function of these organelles: _____

   _____

   _____

   (d) Name the dark 'blobs' attached to the organelle you have labelled:

   _____

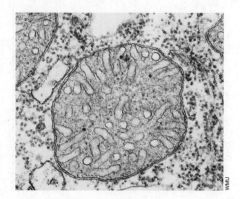

Cell Structure

Code: RA 2

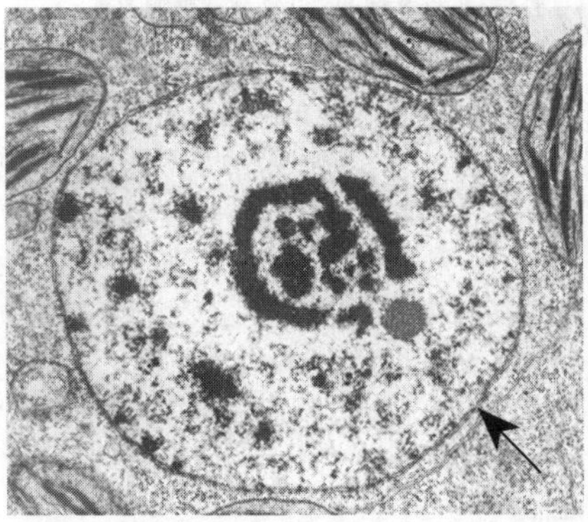

5. (a) Name this large circular structure (arrowed): _____

   (b) State which kind of cell(s) this structure would be found in:

      _____

   (c) Describe the function of this structure: _____

      _____

      _____

   (d) Label three features relating to this structure in the photograph.

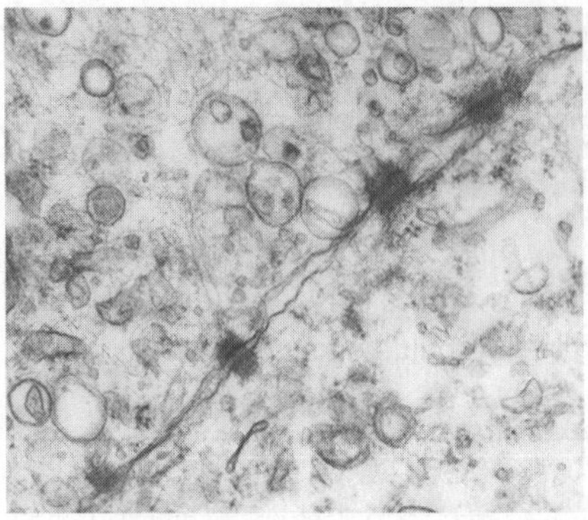

6. The four dark structures shown in this photograph are called **desmosomes**. They cause the plasma membranes of neighbouring cells to stick together. Without desmosomes, animal cells would not combine together to form tissues.

   (a) Describe the functions of the plasma membrane:

      _____

      _____

      _____

   (b) Label the plasma membrane and the four desmosomes in the photograph.

7. In the space below, draw a simple, labelled diagram of a **generalised cell** to show the **relative size** and **location** of these six structures and organelles (simple outlines of the organelles will do):

Identifying Cell Structures

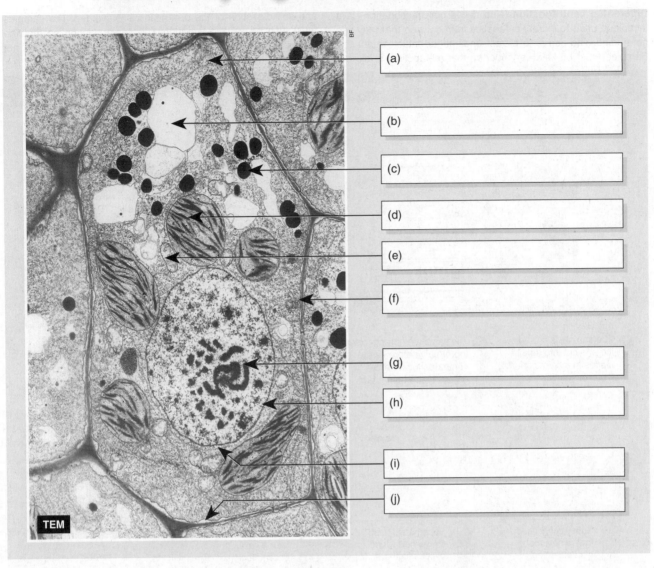

(a) _____

(b) _____

(c) _____

(d) _____

(e) _____

(f) _____

(g) _____

(h) _____

(i) _____

(j) _____

TEM

1. Study the diagrams on the previous pages to become familiar with the various structures found in plant and animal cells. Identify and label the ten structures in the cell above using the following list of terms: *nuclear membrane, cytoplasm, endoplasmic reticulum, mitochondrion, starch granules, chromosome, vacuole, plasma membrane, cell wall, chloroplast*

2. State how many cells, or parts of cells, are visible in the electron micrograph above: _____

3. Identify the **type** of cell illustrated above (bacterial cell, plant cell, or animal cell). Explain your answer:

   _____

   _____

4. (a) Explain where cytoplasm is found in the cell: _____

   _____

   (b) Describe what cytoplasm is made up of: _____

   _____

5. Describe two structures, pictured in the cell above, that are associated with storage:

   (a) _____

   _____

   (b) _____

   _____

Cell Structure

Code: RA 2

Differential Centrifugation

Differential centrifugation (also called cell fractionation) is a technique used to extract organelles from cells so that they can be studied. The aim is to extract undamaged intact organelles. Samples must be kept very cool so that metabolism is slowed and self digestion of the organelles is prevented. The samples must also be kept in a buffered, isotonic solution so that the organelles do not change volume and the enzymes are not denatured by changes in pH.

Differential Centrifugation

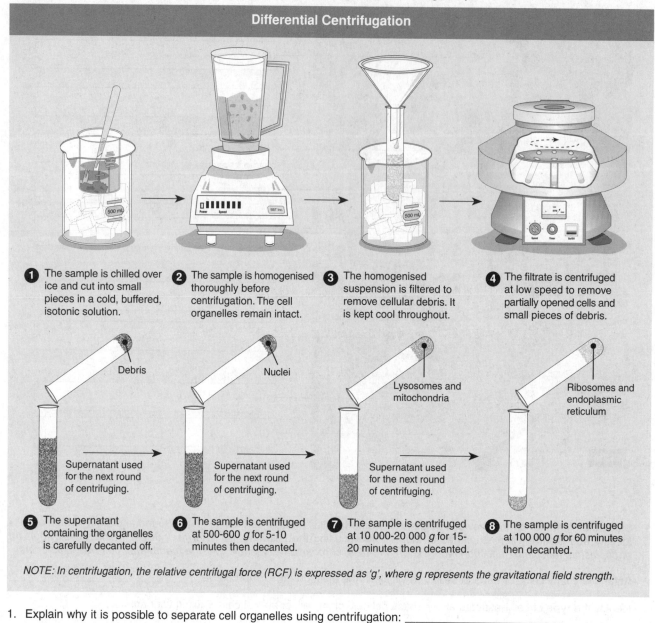

1. The sample is chilled over ice and cut into small pieces in a cold, buffered, isotonic solution.

2. The sample is homogenised thoroughly before centrifugation. The cell organelles remain intact.

3. The homogenised suspension is filtered to remove cellular debris. It is kept cool throughout.

4. The filtrate is centrifuged at low speed to remove partially opened cells and small pieces of debris.

Debris — Supernatant used for the next round of centrifuging.

Nuclei — Supernatant used for the next round of centrifuging.

Lysosomes and mitochondria — Supernatant used for the next round of centrifuging.

Ribosomes and endoplasmic reticulum

5. The supernatant containing the organelles is carefully decanted off.

6. The sample is centrifuged at 500-600 g for 5-10 minutes then decanted.

7. The sample is centrifuged at 10 000-20 000 g for 15-20 minutes then decanted.

8. The sample is centrifuged at 100 000 g for 60 minutes then decanted.

NOTE: In centrifugation, the relative centrifugal force (RCF) is expressed as 'g', where g represents the gravitational field strength.

1. Explain why it is possible to separate cell organelles using centrifugation: _____

_____

_____

2. Suggest why the sample is homogenised before centrifugation: _____

_____

3. Explain why the sample must be kept in a solution that is:

   (a) Isotonic: _____

   (b) Cool: _____

   (c) Buffered: _____

4. **Density gradient centrifugation** is another method of cell fractionation. Sucrose is added to the sample, which is then centrifuged at high speed. The organelles will form layers according to their specific densities. Using the information above, label the centrifuge tube on the right with the organelles you would find in each layer.

Density gradient centrifugation

(a) _____

(b) _____

(c) _____

(d) *Cellular debris*

Plant Cell Specialisation

Plants show a wide variety of cell types. The vegetative plant body consists of three organs: stems, leaves, and roots. Flowers, fruits, and seeds comprise additional organs that are concerned with reproduction. The eight cell types illustrated below are representatives of these plant organ systems. Each has structural or physiological features that set it apart from the other cell types. The differentiation of cells enables each specialised type to fulfil a specific role in the plant.

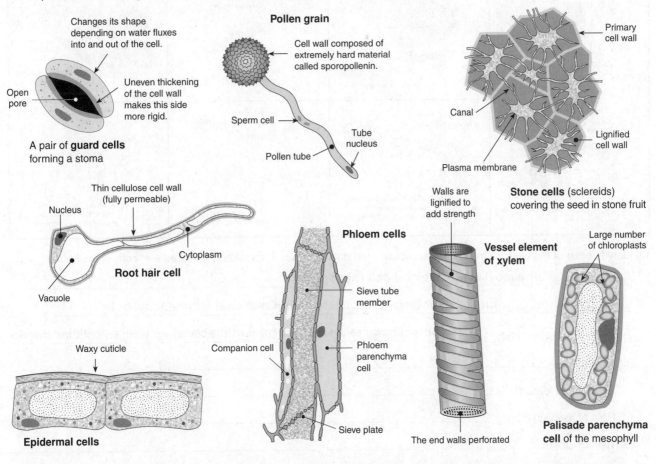

1. Using the information given above, describe the **specialised features** and **role** of each of the cell types (b)-(h) below:

   (a) **Guard cell**: Features: _Curved, sausage-shaped cell, unevenly thickened._

   Role in plant: _Turgor changes alter the cell shape to open or close the stoma._

   (b) **Pollen grain**: Features: _____

   Role in plant: _____

   (c) **Palisade parenchyma cell**: Features: _____

   Role in plant: _____

   (d) **Epidermal cell**: Features: _____

   Role in plant: _____

   (e) **Vessel element**: Features: _____

   Role in plant: _____

   (f) **Stone cell**: Features: _____

   Role in plant: _____

   (g) **Sieve tube member**: Features: _____

   Role in plant: _____

   (h) **Root hair cell**: Features: _____

   Role in plant: _____

Cell Structure

Code: RA 2

Human Cell Specialisation

Animal cells are often specialised to perform particular functions. The eight specialised cell types shown below are representative of some 230 different cell types in humans. Each has specialised features that suit it to performing a specific role.

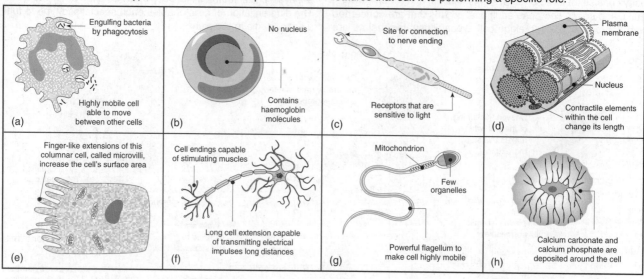

(a) Engulfing bacteria by phagocytosis. Highly mobile cell able to move between other cells

(b) No nucleus. Contains haemoglobin molecules

(c) Site for connection to nerve ending. Receptors that are sensitive to light

(d) Plasma membrane. Nucleus. Contractile elements within the cell change its length

(e) Finger-like extensions of this columnar cell, called microvilli, increase the cell's surface area

(f) Cell endings capable of stimulating muscles. Long cell extension capable of transmitting electrical impulses long distances

(g) Mitochondrion. Few organelles. Powerful flagellum to make cell highly mobile

(h) Calcium carbonate and calcium phosphate are deposited around the cell

1. Identify each of the cells (b) to (h) pictured above, and describe their **specialised features** and **role** in the body:

   (a) Type of cell: _Phagocytic white blood cell (neutrophil)_

       Specialised features: _Engulfs bacteria and other foreign material by phagocytosis_

       Role of cell within body: _Destroys pathogens and other foreign material as well as cellular debris_

   (b) Type of cell: _____

       Specialised features: _____

       Role of cell within body: _____

   (c) Type of cell: _____

       Specialised features: _____

       Role of cell within body: _____

   (d) Type of cell: _____

       Specialised features: _____

       Role of cell within body: _____

   (e) Type of cell: _____

       Specialised features: _____

       Role of cell within body: _____

   (f) Type of cell: _____

       Specialised features: _____

       Role of cell within body: _____

   (g) Type of cell: _____

       Specialised features: _____

       Role of cell within body: _____

   (h) Type of cell: _____

       Specialised features: _____

       Role of cell within body: _____

Levels of Organisation

Organisation is one of the defining features of living things. Organisms are organised according to a hierarchy of structural levels (below), each level building on the one below it. Atoms are organised into complex molecules such as proteins. These form the components of cells. Some organisms consist of single cells, but others are collections of many cells, organised into tissues and organs. Hierarchical organisation allows the grouping of specialised cells together to perform a particular function.

In the spaces provided for each question below, assign each of the examples listed to one of the levels of organisation as indicated.

1. **Animals**: *adrenaline, blood, bone, brain, cardiac muscle, cartilage, collagen, DNA, heart, leucocyte, lysosome, mast cell, nervous system, neurone, phospholipid, reproductive system, ribosomes, Schwann cell, spleen, squamous epithelium.*

(a) Organ system: _____

_____

(b) Organs: _____

_____

(c) Tissues: _____

_____

(d) Cells: _____

_____

(e) Organelles: _____

_____

(f) Molecular level: _____

_____

_____

2. **Plants**: *cellulose, chloroplasts, collenchyma, companion cells, DNA, epidermal cell, fibres, flowers, leaf, mesophyll, parenchyma, pectin, phloem, phospholipid, ribosomes, roots, sclerenchyma, tracheid.*

(a) Organs: _____

_____

(b) Tissues: _____

_____

(c) Cells: _____

_____

(d) Organelles: _____

_____

(e) Molecular level: _____

_____

_____

The Organism
A complex, functioning whole that is the sum of all its component parts.

Organ System Level
In animals, organs form parts of even larger units known as organ systems. An organ system is an association of organs with a common function e.g. digestive system, cardiovascular system, and the urinogenital system.

Organ Level
Organs are structures of definite form and structure, comprising two or more tissues.

Animal examples *include: heart, lungs, brain, stomach, kidney.*

Plant examples *include: leaves, roots, storage organs, ovary.*

Tissue Level
Tissues are composed of groups of cells of similar structure that perform a particular, related function.

Animal examples *include: epithelial tissue, bone, muscle.*

Plant examples *include: phloem, chlorenchyma, endodermis, xylem.*

Cellular Level
Cells are the basic structural and functional units of an organism. Each cell type has a different structure and function; the result of cellular differentiation during development.

Animal examples *include: epithelial cells, osteoblasts, muscle fibres.*

Plant examples *include: sclereids, xylem vessels, sieve tubes.*

Organelle Level
Many diverse molecules may associate together to form complex, highly specialised structures within cells called cellular organelles e.g. mitochondria, Golgi apparatus, endoplasmic reticulum, chloroplasts.

Chemical and Molecular Level
Atoms and molecules form the most basic, level of organisation. This level includes all the chemicals essential for maintaining life e.g. water, ions, fats, carbohydrates, amino acids, proteins, and nucleic acids.

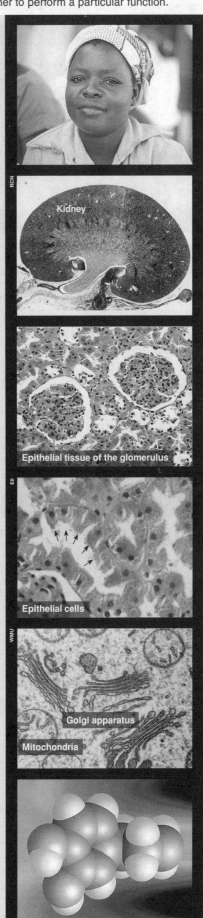

Kidney

Epithelial tissue of the glomerulus

Epithelial cells

Golgi apparatus

Mitochondria

Cell Structure

Code: RA 2

The study of tissues is called **histology**. The cells of a tissue, and their associated intracellular substances e.g. collagen, are grouped together to perform particular functions. Tissues improve the efficiency of operation because they enable tasks to be shared amongst various specialised cells. **Animal tissues** can be divided into four broad groups: **epithelial tissues**, **connective tissues**, **muscle**, and **nervous tissues**. Some features of animal tissues are described below. **Plant tissues** are divided into two groups: **simple** and **complex**. Simple tissues contain only one cell type and form packing and support tissues (e.g. parenchyma). Complex tissues contain more than one cell type and form the conducting and support tissues of plants (periderm, xylem, phloem).

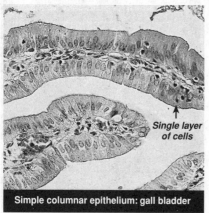

Blood

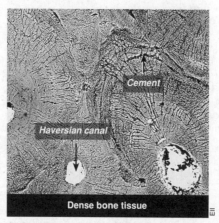

Dense bone tissue

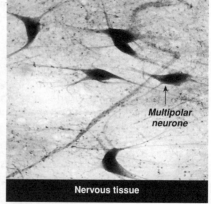

Nervous tissue

Connective tissue is the major supporting tissue of the animal body. It comprises cells, widely dispersed in a semi-fluid matrix. Connective tissues bind other structures together and provide support, and protection against damage, infection, or heat loss. Connective tissues include dentine (teeth), adipose (fat) tissue, bone (above) and cartilage, and the tissues around the body's organs and blood vessels. Blood (above, left) is a special type of liquid tissue, comprising cells floating in a liquid matrix.

Nervous tissue contains densely packed nerve cells (neurones) which are specialised for the transmission of nerve impulses. Associated with the neurones there may also be supporting cells and connective tissue containing blood vessels.

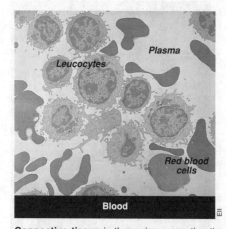

Simple columnar epithelium: gall bladder

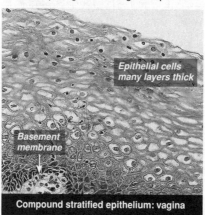

Compound stratified epithelium: vagina

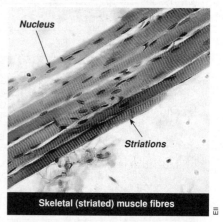

Skeletal (striated) muscle fibres

Epithelial tissue is organised into single (above, left) or layered (above) sheets. It lines internal and external surfaces (e.g. blood vessels, ducts, gut lining) and protects the underlying structures from wear, infection, and/or pressure. Epithelial cells rest on a basement membrane of fibres and collagen and are held together by a carbohydrate-based "glue". The cells may also be specialised for absorption, secretion, or excretion. Examples: stratified (compound) epithelium of vagina, ciliated epithelium of respiratory tract, cuboidal epithelium of kidney ducts, and the columnar epithelium of the intestine.

Muscle tissue consists of very highly specialised cells called fibres, held together by connective tissue. The three types of muscle in the body are cardiac muscle, skeletal muscle (above), and smooth muscle. Muscles bring about both voluntary and involuntary (unconscious) body movements.

3. Explain the advantage of the organisation seen in living things: _____

_____

_____

4. Give an example of an organ system in an animal, stating the organs, tissues, and specialised cells comprising it:

Organ system: _____ Organs: _____

Tissues: _____

Specialised cells: _____

5. Describe the main features of the following animal tissues:

(a) Epithelial tissues: _____

(b) Connective tissues: _____

(c) Muscle tissue: _____

(d) Nervous tissue: _____

Cell Membranes and Transport

Investigating the structure of cell membranes and cellular transport

Cell processes, the structure and role of membranes in cells. Methods of cellular transport, and limitations to cell size.

Learning Objectives

☐ 1. Compile your own glossary from the **KEY WORDS** displayed in **bold type** in the learning objectives below.

Cell Membranes *(pages 23, 61-64)*

☐ 2. Draw a simple labelled diagram of the structure of the **plasma membrane** (cell surface membrane), clearly identifying the arrangement of the lipids and proteins.

☐ 3. Describe and explain the current **fluid-mosaic model** of membrane structure, including the terms **lipid bilayer** and **partially permeable membrane**. Explain the roles of **phospholipids**, **cholesterol**, **glycolipids**, **proteins**, and **glycoproteins** in membrane structure. Recognise that the plasma membrane is essentially no different to the membranes of cellular organelles.

☐ 4. EXTENSION: Outline the evidence from freeze-fracture studies in support of the current model of membrane structure. Contrast this currently accepted model with the earlier Davson-Danielli model.

☐ 5. Describe the general functions of membranes (including the plasma membrane) in the cell, identifying their role in the structure of cellular organelles and their role in regulating the transport of materials within cells, as well as into and out of cells.

Cellular Transport *(pages 60, 65-72)*

☐ 6. Summarise the types of movements that occur across membranes. Outline the role of proteins in membranes as receptors and carriers in membrane transport.

☐ 7. Define: **passive transport**, **concentration gradient**. Describe the processes of **diffusion** and **osmosis**, identifying the types of substances moving in each case.

☐ 8. Describe **facilitated diffusion** (also called facilitated transport). Identify when and where this process might occur in a cell.

☐ 9. Identify factors determining the rate of diffusion. Explain how **Fick's law** provides a framework for determining maximum diffusion rates across cell surfaces.

☐ 10. Suggest why cell size is limited by the rate of diffusion. Discuss the significance of **surface area to volume ratio** to cells. Explain why organisms without efficient transport mechanisms remain small.

☐ 11. Explain what is meant by **water potential** (ψ) and identify its significance to the net movement of water in cells. Define the components of water potential: **solute potential** and **pressure potential**.

☐ 12. EXTENSION: Determine the net direction of water movement between solutions of different ψ.

☐ 13. With respect to plant cells, define the terms: **turgor** and **plasmolysis**. With respect to solutions of differing solute concentration, distinguish between: **hypotonic**, **isotonic**, **hypertonic**. Comment on the importance of ion concentrations in maintaining cell turgor.

☐ 14. Distinguish between passive and **active transport** mechanisms. Understand the principles involved in active transport, clearly identifying the involvement of protein molecules and energy.

☐ 15. Describe the following active transport mechanisms: **ion-exchange pumps**, **exocytosis**, **endocytosis**, **phagocytosis**, and **pinocytosis**. Give examples of when and where (in the plant or animal body) each type of transport mechanism occurs.

☐ 16. Identify the mechanisms involved in the transport of some of the most important substances: water, fatty acids, glucose, amino acids, O_2, CO_2, ions (e.g. mineral and metal ions), sucrose (in plants).

Supplementary Texts

See page 7 for details of these texts:

■ Adds, J., *et al.*, 2003. **Molecules and Cells**, (NelsonThornes), chpt. 4 as required.

■ Harwood, R., 2002. **Biochemistry**, (Cambridge University Press), chpt. 5.

■ Tobin, A.J. and Morel, R.E., 1997. **Asking About Cells**, (Thomson Brooks/Cole), as required.

Cell Biology & Biochemistry

Presentation MEDIA to support this topic:

CELL BIO & BIOCHEM Cell Membranes & Transport

Periodicals

See page 7 for details of publishers of periodicals:

STUDENT'S REFERENCE

■ **Cellular Factories** New Scientist, 23 Nov. 1996 (Inside Science). *An overview of cellular processes and the role of organelles in plant and animal cells.*

■ **Osmosis and Water Retention in Plants** Biol. Sci. Rev., 7(3) January 1995, pp. 14-16. *A good explanation of osmosis, water and solute potential and water movement in and around plant cells.*

■ **Water Channels in the Cell Membrane** Biol. Sci. Rev., 9(2) November 1996, pp. 18-22. *The role of proteins in membrane transport, including the mechanisms involved in physiological processes.*

■ **Water, Water, Everywhere...** Biol. Sci. Rev., 7(5) May 1995, pp. 6-9. *The transport of water in plants (turgor, bulk flow and water potential).*

Internet

See pages 4-5 for details of how to access **Bio Links** from our web site: **www.thebiozone.com** From Bio Links, access sites under the topics:

GENERAL BIOLOGY ONLINE RESOURCES • Biology I interactive animations • Instructional multimedia, University of Alberta • HowStuffWorks • Biointeractive *... and others* > **Online Textbooks and Lecture Notes**: • S-Cool! A level biology revision guide Learn.co.uk *... and others* > **Glossaries**: • Cellular biology: Glossary of terms • Kimball's biology glossary *... and others*

CELL BIOLOGY AND BIOCHEMISTRY: • Cell and molecular biology online > **Cell Structure and Transport**: • Aquaporins • CELLS alive! • The virtual cell • Transport in and out of cells

Cell Processes

All of the organelles and other structures in the cell have functions. The cell can be compared to a factory with an assembly line. Organelles in the cell provide the equivalent of the power supply, assembly line, packaging department, repair and maintenance, transport system, and the control centre. The sum total of all the processes occurring in a cell is known as **metabolism**. Some of these processes store energy in molecules (anabolism) while others release that stored energy (catabolism). Below is a summary of the major processes that take place in a cell.

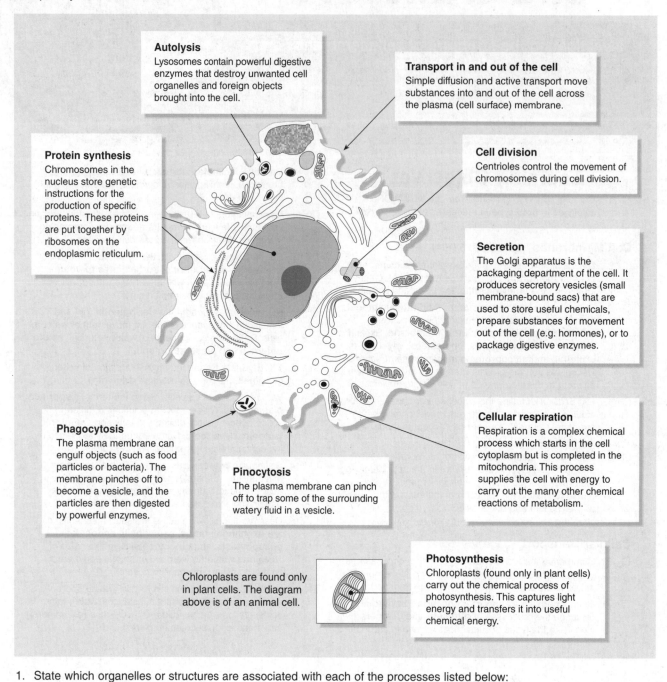

Autolysis
Lysosomes contain powerful digestive enzymes that destroy unwanted cell organelles and foreign objects brought into the cell.

Transport in and out of the cell
Simple diffusion and active transport move substances into and out of the cell across the plasma (cell surface) membrane.

Protein synthesis
Chromosomes in the nucleus store genetic instructions for the production of specific proteins. These proteins are put together by ribosomes on the endoplasmic reticulum.

Cell division
Centrioles control the movement of chromosomes during cell division.

Secretion
The Golgi apparatus is the packaging department of the cell. It produces secretory vesicles (small membrane-bound sacs) that are used to store useful chemicals, prepare substances for movement out of the cell (e.g. hormones), or to package digestive enzymes.

Phagocytosis
The plasma membrane can engulf objects (such as food particles or bacteria). The membrane pinches off to become a vesicle, and the particles are then digested by powerful enzymes.

Pinocytosis
The plasma membrane can pinch off to trap some of the surrounding watery fluid in a vesicle.

Cellular respiration
Respiration is a complex chemical process which starts in the cell cytoplasm but is completed in the mitochondria. This process supplies the cell with energy to carry out the many other chemical reactions of metabolism.

Chloroplasts are found only in plant cells. The diagram above is of an animal cell.

Photosynthesis
Chloroplasts (found only in plant cells) carry out the chemical process of photosynthesis. This captures light energy and transfers it into useful chemical energy.

1. State which organelles or structures are associated with each of the processes listed below:

   (a) Secretion: _____

   (b) Respiration: _____

   (c) Pinocytosis: _____

   (d) Phagocytosis: _____

   (e) Protein synthesis: _____

   (f) Photosynthesis: _____

   (g) Cell division: _____

   (h) Autolysis: _____

   (i) Transport in/out of cell: _____

2. Explain what is meant by **metabolism** and describe an example of a metabolic process: _____
   _____
   _____

The Structure of Membranes

All cells have a plasma membrane that forms the outer limit of the cell. Bacteria, fungi, and plant cells have a cell wall outside this, but it is quite distinct and outside the cell. Membranes are also found inside eukaryotic cells as part of membranous **organelles**. Present day knowledge of membrane structure has been built up as a result of many observations and experiments. The original model of membrane structure, proposed by Davson and Danielli, was the unit membrane; a lipid bilayer coated with protein. This model was later modified after the discovery that the protein molecules were embedded within the bilayer rather than coating the outside. The now-accepted model of membrane structure is the **fluid-mosaic model** described below.

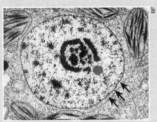

The **nuclear membrane** that surrounds the nucleus helps to control the passage of genetic information to the cytoplasm. It may also serve to protect the DNA.

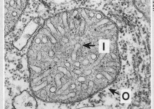

Mitochondria have an outer membrane (**O**) which controls the entry and exit of materials involved in aerobic respiration. Inner membranes (**I**) provide attachment sites for enzyme activity.

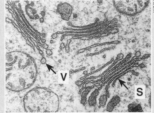

The **Golgi apparatus** comprises stacks of membrane-bound sacs (**S**). It is involved in packaging materials for transport or export from the cell as secretory vesicles (**V**).

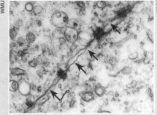

The cell is surrounded by a **plasma membrane** which controls the movement of most substances into and out of the cell. This photo shows two neighbouring cells (arrows).

The Fluid Mosaic Model

The currently accepted model for the structure of membranes is called the **fluid mosaic model**. In this model there is a double layer of lipids (fats) which are arranged with their 'tails' facing inwards. The double layer of lipids is thought to be quite fluid, with proteins 'floating' in this layer. The mobile proteins are thought to have a number of functions, including a role in active transport.

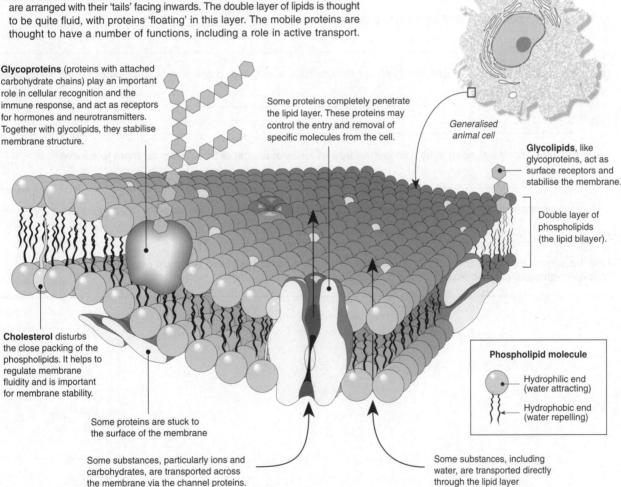

Glycoproteins (proteins with attached carbohydrate chains) play an important role in cellular recognition and the immune response, and act as receptors for hormones and neurotransmitters. Together with glycolipids, they stabilise membrane structure.

Some proteins completely penetrate the lipid layer. These proteins may control the entry and removal of specific molecules from the cell.

Generalised animal cell

Glycolipids, like glycoproteins, act as surface receptors and stabilise the membrane.

Double layer of phospholipids (the lipid bilayer).

Cholesterol disturbs the close packing of the phospholipids. It helps to regulate membrane fluidity and is important for membrane stability.

Some proteins are stuck to the surface of the membrane

Some substances, particularly ions and carbohydrates, are transported across the membrane via the channel proteins.

Some substances, including water, are transported directly through the lipid layer

Phospholipid molecule

Hydrophilic end (water attracting)

Hydrophobic end (water repelling)

1. (a) Describe the modern fluid mosaic model of membrane structure: _____

_____

_____

_____

62

(b) Explain how the modern fluid mosaic model of membrane structure differs from the earlier Davson-Danielli model:

_____

_____

_____

2. Discuss the various functional roles of membranes in cells: _____

_____

_____

_____

3. (a) Name a cellular organelle that possesses a membrane: _____

(b) Describe the membrane's purpose in this organelle: _____

_____

4. Identify three other cell organelles that are made up of membrane systems:

(a) _____

(b) _____

(c) _____

5. (a) Describe the purpose of cholesterol in plasma membranes: _____

_____

(b) Suggest why marine organisms living in polar regions have a very high proportion of cholesterol in their membranes:

_____

_____

6. List three substances that need to be transported **into** all kinds of animal cells, in order for them to survive:

(a) _____ (b) _____ (c) _____

7. List two substances that need to be transported **out** of all kinds of animal cells, in order for them to survive:

(a) _____ (b) _____

8. Use the symbol for a phospholipid molecule (below) to draw a **simple labelled diagram** to show the structure of a plasma membrane (include features such as lipid bilayer and various kinds of proteins):

Symbol for phospholipid

The Role of Membranes in Cells

Many of the important structures and organelles in cells are composed of, or are enclosed by, membranes. These include: the endoplasmic reticulum, mitochondria, nucleus, Golgi apparatus, chloroplasts, lysosomes, vesicles and the plasma membrane itself. All membranes within eukaryotic cells share the same basic structure as the plasma membrane that encloses the entire cell. They perform a number of critical functions in the cell: serving to compartmentalise regions of different function within the cell, controlling the entry and exit of substances, and fulfilling a role in recognition and communication between cells. Some of these roles are described below. The role of membranes in the production of macromolecules is shown on the following page:

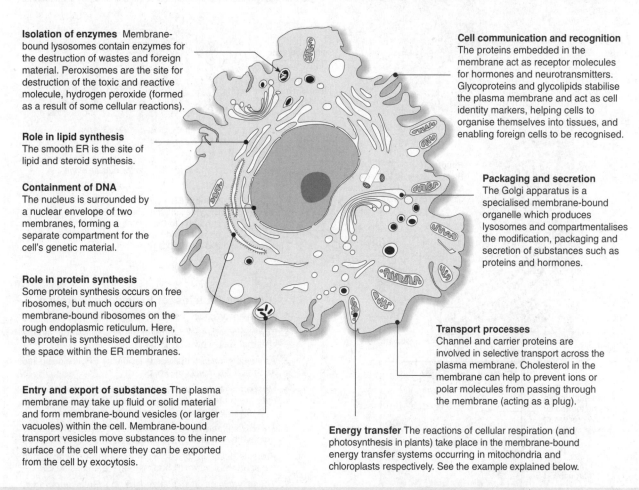

Isolation of enzymes Membrane-bound lysosomes contain enzymes for the destruction of wastes and foreign material. Peroxisomes are the site for destruction of the toxic and reactive molecule, hydrogen peroxide (formed as a result of some cellular reactions).

Role in lipid synthesis
The smooth ER is the site of lipid and steroid synthesis.

Containment of DNA
The nucleus is surrounded by a nuclear envelope of two membranes, forming a separate compartment for the cell's genetic material.

Role in protein synthesis
Some protein synthesis occurs on free ribosomes, but much occurs on membrane-bound ribosomes on the rough endoplasmic reticulum. Here, the protein is synthesised directly into the space within the ER membranes.

Entry and export of substances The plasma membrane may take up fluid or solid material and form membrane-bound vesicles (or larger vacuoles) within the cell. Membrane-bound transport vesicles move substances to the inner surface of the cell where they can be exported from the cell by exocytosis.

Cell communication and recognition
The proteins embedded in the membrane act as receptor molecules for hormones and neurotransmitters. Glycoproteins and glycolipids stabilise the plasma membrane and act as cell identity markers, helping cells to organise themselves into tissues, and enabling foreign cells to be recognised.

Packaging and secretion
The Golgi apparatus is a specialised membrane-bound organelle which produces lysosomes and compartmentalises the modification, packaging and secretion of substances such as proteins and hormones.

Transport processes
Channel and carrier proteins are involved in selective transport across the plasma membrane. Cholesterol in the membrane can help to prevent ions or polar molecules from passing through the membrane (acting as a plug).

Energy transfer The reactions of cellular respiration (and photosynthesis in plants) take place in the membrane-bound energy transfer systems occurring in mitochondria and chloroplasts respectively. See the example explained below.

Compartmentation within Membranes

Membranes play an important role in separating regions within the cell (and within organelles) where particular reactions occur. Specific enzymes are therefore often located in particular organelles. The reaction rate is controlled by controlling the rate at which substrates enter the organelle and therefore the availability of the raw materials required for the reactions.

Example (right): *The enzymes involved in cellular respiration are arranged in different parts of the mitochondria. Reactions are localised and separated by membrane systems.*

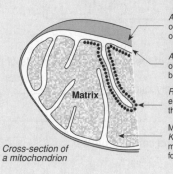

Amine oxidases and other enzymes on the outer membrane surface

Adenylate kinase and other *phosphorylases* between the membranes

Respiratory assembly enzymes embedded in the membrane (ATPase)

Many soluble enzymes of the *Krebs cycle* floating in the matrix, as well as enzymes for fatty acid degradation.

Matrix

Cross-section of a mitochondrion

1. Explain the crucial role of membrane systems and organelles in the following:

   (a) Providing compartments within the cell: _____

   _____

   _____

   (b) Increasing the total membrane surface area within the cell: _____

   _____

   _____

   _____

Code: A 2

Cells produce a range of **macromolecules**; organic polymers made up of repeating units of smaller molecules. The synthesis, packaging and movement of these molecules inside the cell involves a number of membrane bound organelles, as indicated below. These organelles provide compartments where the enzyme systems involved can be isolated.

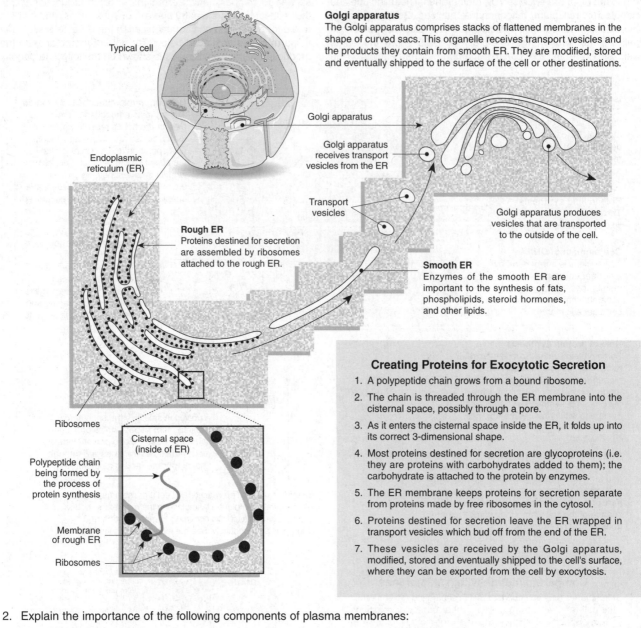

Typical cell

Endoplasmic reticulum (ER)

Golgi apparatus

Golgi apparatus
The Golgi apparatus comprises stacks of flattened membranes in the shape of curved sacs. This organelle receives transport vesicles and the products they contain from smooth ER. They are modified, stored and eventually shipped to the surface of the cell or other destinations.

Golgi apparatus receives transport vesicles from the ER

Transport vesicles

Golgi apparatus produces vesicles that are transported to the outside of the cell.

Rough ER
Proteins destined for secretion are assembled by ribosomes attached to the rough ER.

Smooth ER
Enzymes of the smooth ER are important to the synthesis of fats, phospholipids, steroid hormones, and other lipids.

Ribosomes

Cisternal space (inside of ER)

Polypeptide chain being formed by the process of protein synthesis

Membrane of rough ER

Ribosomes

Creating Proteins for Exocytotic Secretion

1. A polypeptide chain grows from a bound ribosome.

2. The chain is threaded through the ER membrane into the cisternal space, possibly through a pore.

3. As it enters the cisternal space inside the ER, it folds up into its correct 3-dimensional shape.

4. Most proteins destined for secretion are glycoproteins (i.e. they are proteins with carbohydrates added to them); the carbohydrate is attached to the protein by enzymes.

5. The ER membrane keeps proteins for secretion separate from proteins made by free ribosomes in the cytosol.

6. Proteins destined for secretion leave the ER wrapped in transport vesicles which bud off from the end of the ER.

7. These vesicles are received by the Golgi apparatus, modified, stored and eventually shipped to the cell's surface, where they can be exported from the cell by exocytosis.

2. Explain the importance of the following components of plasma membranes:

(a) Glycoproteins and glycolipids: _____

_____

(b) Channel proteins and carrier proteins: _____

_____

3. Explain how cholesterol can play a role in membrane transport: _____

_____

4. Non-polar (lipid-soluble) molecules diffuse more rapidly through membranes than polar (lipid-insoluble) molecules:

(a) Explain the reason for this: _____

_____

(b) Discuss the implications of this to the transport of substances into the cell through the plasma membrane:

_____

_____

Active and Passive Transport

Cells have a need to move materials both into and out of the cell. Raw materials and other molecules necessary for metabolism must be accumulated from outside the cell. Some of these substances are scarce outside of the cell and some effort is required to accumulate them. Waste products and molecules for use in other parts of the body must be 'exported' out of the cell.

Some materials (e.g. gases and water) move into and out of the cell by **passive transport** processes, without the expenditure of energy on the part of the cell. Other molecules (e.g. sucrose) are moved into and out of the cell using **active transport**. Active transport processes involve the expenditure of energy in the form of ATP, and therefore use oxygen.

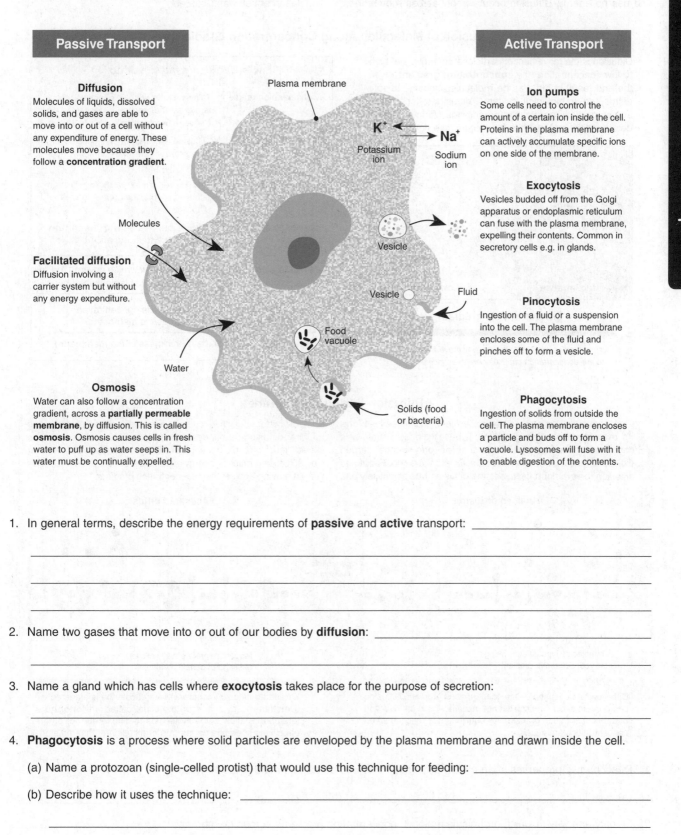

Passive Transport

Diffusion
Molecules of liquids, dissolved solids, and gases are able to move into or out of a cell without any expenditure of energy. These molecules move because they follow a **concentration gradient**.

Molecules

Facilitated diffusion
Diffusion involving a carrier system but without any energy expenditure.

Water

Osmosis
Water can also follow a concentration gradient, across a **partially permeable membrane**, by diffusion. This is called **osmosis**. Osmosis causes cells in fresh water to puff up as water seeps in. This water must be continually expelled.

Plasma membrane

K⁺ Potassium ion → ← Na⁺ Sodium ion

Vesicle

Vesicle   Fluid

Food vacuole

Solids (food or bacteria)

Active Transport

Ion pumps
Some cells need to control the amount of a certain ion inside the cell. Proteins in the plasma membrane can actively accumulate specific ions on one side of the membrane.

Exocytosis
Vesicles budded off from the Golgi apparatus or endoplasmic reticulum can fuse with the plasma membrane, expelling their contents. Common in secretory cells e.g. in glands.

Pinocytosis
Ingestion of a fluid or a suspension into the cell. The plasma membrane encloses some of the fluid and pinches off to form a vesicle.

Phagocytosis
Ingestion of solids from outside the cell. The plasma membrane encloses a particle and buds off to form a vacuole. Lysosomes will fuse with it to enable digestion of the contents.

1. In general terms, describe the energy requirements of **passive** and **active** transport: _____

_____

_____

_____

2. Name two gases that move into or out of our bodies by **diffusion**: _____

_____

3. Name a gland which has cells where **exocytosis** takes place for the purpose of secretion: _____

_____

4. **Phagocytosis** is a process where solid particles are enveloped by the plasma membrane and drawn inside the cell.

    (a) Name a protozoan (single-celled protist) that would use this technique for feeding: _____

    (b) Describe how it uses the technique: _____

    _____

    (c) Name a type of cell found in human blood that uses this technique for capturing and destroying bacteria:

    _____

Code: RA 1

Diffusion

The molecules that make up substances are constantly moving about in a random way. This random motion causes molecules to disperse from areas of high to low concentration; a process called **diffusion**. The molecules move along a **concentration gradient**. Diffusion and osmosis (diffusion of water molecules across a partially permeable membrane) are **passive** processes, and use no energy. Diffusion occurs freely across membranes, as long as the membrane is permeable to that molecule (partially permeable membranes allow the passage of some molecules but not others). Each type of molecule diffuses along its own concentration gradient. Diffusion of molecules in one direction does not hinder the movement of other molecules. Diffusion is important in allowing exchanges with the environment and in the regulation of cell water content.

Diffusion of Molecules Along Concentration Gradients

Diffusion is the movement of particles from regions of high to low concentration (the **concentration gradient**), with the end result being that the molecules become evenly distributed. In biological systems, diffusion often occurs across partially permeable membranes. Various factors determine the rate at which this occurs (see right).

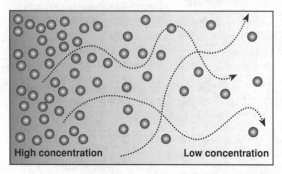

High concentration   **Low concentration**

Concentration gradient

If molecules are free to move, they move from high to low concentration until they are evenly dispersed.

Factors affecting rates of diffusion	
Concentration gradient:	Diffusion rates will be higher when there is a greater difference in concentration between two regions.
The distance involved:	Diffusion over shorter distances occurs at a greater rate than diffusion over larger distances.
The area involved:	The larger the area across which diffusion occurs, the greater the rate of diffusion.
Barriers to diffusion:	Thicker barriers slow diffusion rate. Pores in a barrier enhance diffusion.

These factors are expressed in **Fick's law**, which governs the rate of diffusion of substances within a system. It is described by:

$$\frac{\text{Surface area of membrane} \times \text{Difference in concentration across the membrane}}{\text{Length of the diffusion path (thickness of the membrane)}}$$

Diffusion through Membranes

Each type of diffusing molecule (gas, solvent, solute) moves **along its own concentration gradient**. Two-way diffusion (below) is common in biological systems, e.g. at the lung surface, carbon dioxide diffuses out and oxygen diffuses into the blood. Facilitated diffusion (below, right) increases the diffusion rate selectively and is important for larger molecules (e.g. glucose, amino acids) where a higher diffusion rate is desirable (e.g. transport of glucose into skeletal muscle fibres, transport of ADP into mitochondria). Neither type of diffusion requires energy expenditure because the molecules are not moving against their concentration gradient.

Unaided diffusion

Partially permeable membrane

Each molecule type diffuses along its own concentration gradient.

Facilitated diffusion

Ionophore

Ionophore preferentially allows passage of certain molecules.

Diffusion rates depend on the concentration gradient. Diffusion can occur in either direction but **net** movement is in the direction of the concentration gradient. An equilibrium is reached when concentrations are equal.

Facilitated diffusion occurs when a substance is aided across a membrane by a special molecule called an **ionophore**. Ionophores allow some molecules to diffuse but not others, effectively speeding up the rate of diffusion of that molecule.

1. Describe two properties of an exchange surface that would facilitate rapid diffusion rates:

   (a) _____   (b) _____

2. Identify one way in which organisms maintain concentration gradients across membranes: _____
   _____

3. State how facilitated diffusion is achieved: _____

Osmosis and Water Potential

Osmosis is the term describing the diffusion of water along its concentration gradient across a partially permeable membrane. It is the principal mechanism by which water enters and leaves cells in living organisms. As it is a type of diffusion, the rate at which osmosis occurs is affected by the same factors that affect all diffusion rates (see earlier). The tendency for water to move in any particular direction can be calculated on the basis of the water potential of the cell sap relative to its surrounding environment. The use of water potential to express the water relations of cells has replaced the terms osmotic potential and osmotic pressure although these are still frequently used in areas of animal physiology and medicine. The concepts of osmosis, water potential, cell turgor, and plasmolysis are explained below and on the following page.

Osmosis and the Water Potential of Cells

Osmosis is simply the diffusion of water molecules from high concentration to lower concentration, across a partially permeable membrane. The direction of this movement can be predicted on the basis of the water potential of the solutions involved. The **water potential** of a solution (denoted with the symbol ψ) is the term given to the tendency for water molecules to enter or leave a solution by osmosis. Pure water has the highest water potential, set at zero. Dissolving any solute into pure water lowers the water potential (makes it more negative). *Water always diffuses from regions of less negative to more negative water potential.* Water potential is determined by two components: the **solute potential**, ψs (of the cell sap) and the **pressure potential**, ψp. This is expressed as a simple equation:

$$\psi cell = \psi s + \psi p$$

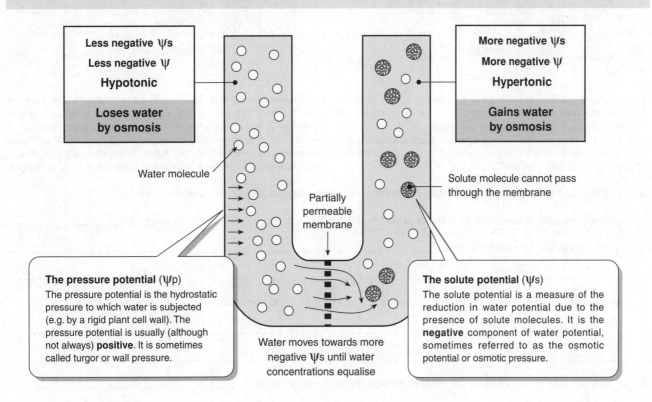

The pressure potential (ψp): The pressure potential is the hydrostatic pressure to which water is subjected (e.g. by a rigid plant cell wall). The pressure potential is usually (although not always) **positive**. It is sometimes called turgor or wall pressure.

Water moves towards more negative ψs until water concentrations equalise

The solute potential (ψs): The solute potential is a measure of the reduction in water potential due to the presence of solute molecules. It is the **negative** component of water potential, sometimes referred to as the osmotic potential or osmotic pressure.

1. State the water potential of pure water at standard temperature and pressure: _____

2. The three diagrams below show the solute and pressure potential values for three hypothetical situations where two solutions are separated by a selectively permeable membrane. For each example (a)-(c) calculate ψ for the solutions on each side of the membrane, as indicated:

3. Draw arrows on each diagram to indicate the direction of net flow of water:

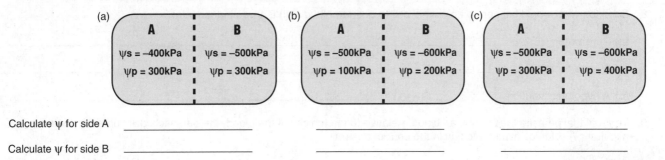

Calculate ψ for side A _____

Calculate ψ for side B _____

Code: DA 2

Water Relations in Plant Cells

The plasma membrane of cells is a partially permeable membrane and osmosis is the principal mechanism by which water enters and leaves the cell. When the external water potential is the same as that of the cell there is no net movement of water. Two systems (cell and environment) with the same water potential are termed **isotonic**. The diagram below illustrates two different situations: when the external water potential is less negative than the cell (**hypotonic**) and when it is more negative than the cell (**hypertonic**).

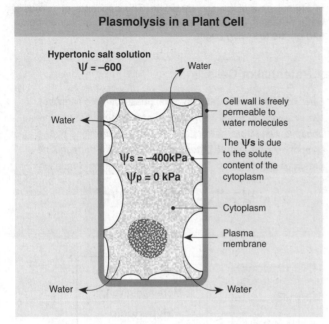

Plasmolysis in a Plant Cell

Hypertonic salt solution
$\Psi = -600$

Water

Water

$\Psi s = -400kPa$

$\Psi p = 0$ kPa

Cell wall is freely permeable to water molecules

The Ψs is due to the solute content of the cytoplasm

Cytoplasm

Plasma membrane

Water

Water

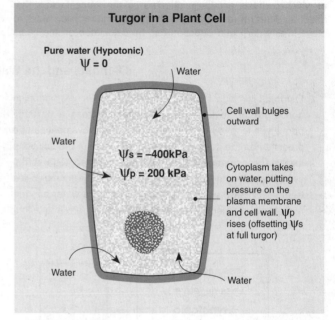

Turgor in a Plant Cell

Pure water (Hypotonic)
$\Psi = 0$

Water

Water

$\Psi s = -400kPa$

$\Psi p = 200$ kPa

Cell wall bulges outward

Cytoplasm takes on water, putting pressure on the plasma membrane and cell wall. Ψp rises (offsetting Ψs at full turgor)

Water

Water

In a **hypertonic** solution, the external water potential is more negative than the water potential of the cell ($\Psi cell = \Psi s + \Psi p$). Water leaves the cell and, because the cell wall is rigid, the plasma membrane shrinks away from the cell wall. This process is termed **plasmolysis** and the cell becomes **flaccid** ($\Psi p = 0$). Full plasmolysis is irreversible; the cell cannot recover by taking up water.

In a **hypotonic** solution, the external water potential is less negative than the $\Psi cell$. Water enters the cell causing it to swell tight. A pressure potential is generated when sufficient water has been taken up to cause the cell contents to press against the cell wall. Ψp rises progressively until it offsets Ψs. Water uptake stops when $\Psi cell = 0$. The rigid cell wall prevents cell rupture. Cells in this state are **turgid**.

4. Fluid replacements are usually provided for heavily perspiring athletes after endurance events.

    (a) Identify the preferable tonicity of these replacement drinks (isotonic, hypertonic, or hypotonic): _____

    (b) Give a reason for your answer: _____

    _____

5. *Paramecium* is a freshwater protozoan. Describe the problem it has in controlling the amount of water inside the cell:

    _____

    _____

6. (a) Explain the role of pressure potential in generating cell turgor in plants: _____

    _____

    (b) Explain the purpose of cell turgor to plants: _____

    _____

7. Explain how animal cells differ from plant cells with respect to the effects of net water movements: _____

    _____

8. Describe what would happen to an animal cell (e.g. a red blood cell) if it was placed into:

    (a) Pure water: _____

    (b) A hypertonic solution: _____

    (c) A hypotonic solution: _____

9. The malarial parasite lives in human blood. Relative to the tonicity of the blood, the parasite's cell contents would be hypotonic / isotonic / hypertonic (circle the correct answer).

Limitations to Cell Size

When an object (e.g. a cell) is small it has a large surface area in comparison to its volume. In this case diffusion will be an effective way to transport materials (e.g. gases) into the cell. As an object becomes larger, its surface area compared to its volume is smaller. Diffusion is no longer an effective way to transport materials to the inside. For this reason, there is a physical limit for the size of a cell, with the effectiveness of diffusion being the controlling factor.

Diffusion in Organisms of Different Sizes

Respiratory gases and some other substances are exchanged with the surroundings by diffusion or active transport across the plasma membrane.

The **plasma membrane**, which surrounds every cell, functions as a selective barrier that regulates the cell's chemical composition. For each square micrometre of membrane, only so much of a particular substance can cross per second.

The surface area of an elephant is increased, for radiating body heat, by large flat ears.

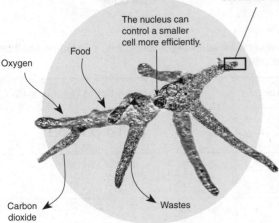
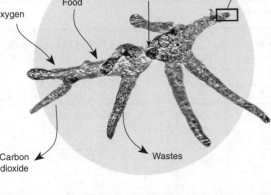

The nucleus can control a smaller cell more efficiently.

Oxygen

Food

Carbon dioxide

Wastes

A specialised gas exchange surface (lungs) and circulatory (blood) system are required to speed up the movement of substances through the body.

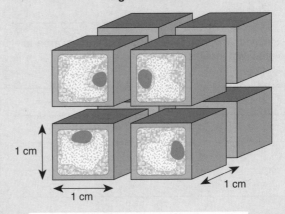

Respiratory gases cannot reach body tissues by diffusion alone.

Amoeba: The small size of single-celled protoctists, such as *Amoeba*, provides a large surface area relative to the cell's volume. This is adequate for many materials to be moved into and out of the cell by diffusion or active transport.

Multicellular organisms: To overcome the problems of small cell size, plants and animals became multicellular. They provide a small surface area compared to their volume but have evolved various adaptive features to improve their effective surface area.

Smaller is Better for Diffusion

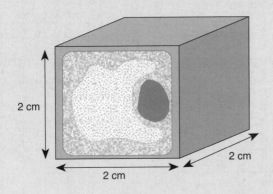

One large cube

2 cm

2 cm

2 cm

Volume: = 8 cm³
Surface area: = 24 cm²

Eight small cubes

1 cm

1 cm

1 cm

Volume: = 8 cm³ for 8 cubes
Surface area: = 6 cm² for 1 cube
= 48 cm² for 8 cubes

The eight small cells and the single large cell have the same total volume, but their surface areas are different. The small cells together have twice the total surface area of the large cell, because there are more exposed (inner) surfaces. Real organisms have complex shapes, but the same principles apply.

The surface-area volume relationship has important implications for processes involving transport into and out of cells across membranes. For activities such as gas exchange, the surface area available for diffusion is a major factor limiting the rate at which oxygen can be supplied to tissues.

Code: DA 1

The diagram below shows four imaginary cells of different sizes (cells do not actually grow to this size, their large size is for the sake of the exercise). They range from a small 2 cm cube to a larger 5 cm cube. This exercise investigates the effect of cell size on the efficiency of diffusion.

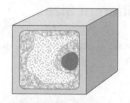
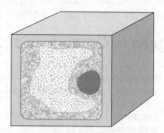
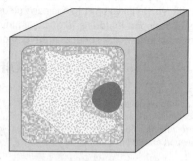

2 cm cube   **3 cm cube**   **4 cm cube**   **5 cm cube**

1. Calculate the volume, surface area and the ratio of surface area to volume for each of the four cubes above (the first has been done for you). When completing the table below, show your calculations.

Cube size	Surface area	Volume	Surface area to volume ratio
2 cm cube	$2 \times 2 \times 6 = 24\ cm^2$ <small>(2 cm x 2 cm x 6 sides)</small>	$2 \times 2 \times 2 = 8\ cm^3$ <small>(height x width x depth)</small>	24 to 8 = 3:1
3 cm cube			
4 cm cube			
5 cm cube			

2. Create a graph, plotting the surface area against the volume of each cube, on the grid on the right. Draw a line connecting the points and label axes and units.

3. State which increases the fastest with increasing size, the **volume** or **surface area**.

_____

4. Explain what happens to the ratio of surface area to volume with increasing size:

_____

_____

_____

_____

5. Diffusion of substances into and out of a cell occurs across the cell surface. Describe how increasing the size of a cell will affect the ability of diffusion to transport materials into and out of a cell:

_____

_____

_____

_____

Ion Pumps

Diffusion alone cannot supply the cell's entire requirements for molecules (and ions). Some molecules (e.g. glucose) are required by the cell in higher concentrations than occur outside the cell. Others (e.g. sodium) must be removed from the cell in order to maintain cell fluid balance. These molecules must be moved across the plasma membrane by active transport mechanisms. **Active transport** requires the expenditure of energy because the molecules (or ions) must be moved **against** their concentration gradient. The work of active transport is performed by specific carrier proteins in the membrane. These transport proteins harness the energy of ATP to pump molecules from a low to a high concentration. When ATP transfers a phosphate group to the carrier protein, the protein changes its shape in such a way as to move the bound molecule across the membrane. Three types of membrane pump are illustrated below. The sodium-potassium pump (below, left) is almost universal in animal cells and is common in plant cells also. The concentration gradient created by ion pumps such as this and the proton pump (centre) is frequently coupled to the transport of other molecules such as glucose and sucrose (below, right).

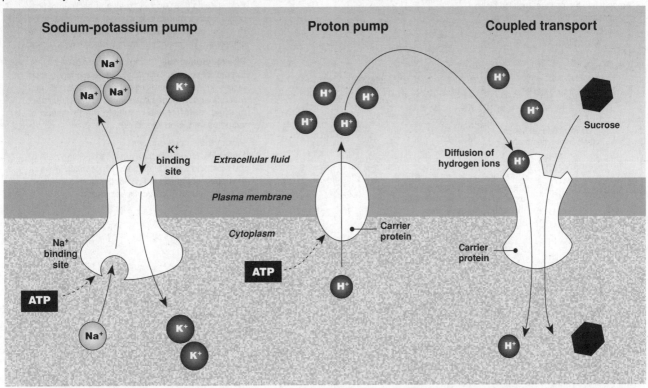

Sodium-potassium pump
The sodium-potassium pump is a specific protein in the membrane that uses energy in the form of ATP to exchange sodium ions (Na^+) for potassium ions (K^+) across the membrane. The unequal balance of Na^+ and K^+ across the membrane creates large concentration gradients that can be used to drive other active transport mechanisms.

Proton pumps
ATP driven proton pumps use energy to remove hydrogen ions (H^+) from inside the cell to the outside. This creates a large difference in the proton concentration either side of the membrane, with the inside of the plasma membrane being negatively charged. This potential difference can be coupled to the transport of other molecules.

Coupled transport (cotransport)
Plant cells use the gradient in hydrogen ions created by proton pumps to drive the active transport of nutrients into the cell. The specific transport protein couples the return of H^+ to the transport of sucrose into the phloem cells. The sucrose rides with the H^+ as it diffuses down the concentration gradient maintained by the proton pump.

1. The sodium-potassium pump plays an important role in the water balance of cells. In terms of osmosis, explain the consequences of the sodium-potassium pumps not working:

_____

_____

2. Explain how the transport of molecules such as sucrose can be coupled to the activity of an ion exchange pump:

_____

_____

_____

3. Explain why the ATP is required for membrane pump systems to operate: _____

_____

_____

4. Name a type of cell that relies on coupled transport to perform its function: _____

Code: A 2

Exocytosis and Endocytosis

Most cells carry out **cytosis**: a form of **active transport** involving the in- or outfolding of the plasma membrane. The ability of cells to do this is a function of the flexibility of the plasma membrane. Cytosis results in the bulk transport into or out of the cell and is achieved through the localised activity of microfilaments and microtubules in the cell cytoskeleton. Engulfment of material is termed **endocytosis.** Endocytosis typically occurs in protozoans and certain white blood cells of the mammalian defence system (e.g. neutrophils, macrophages). **Exocytosis** is the reverse of endocytosis and involves the release of material from vesicles or vacuoles that have fused with the plasma membrane. Exocytosis is typical of cells that export material (secretory cells).

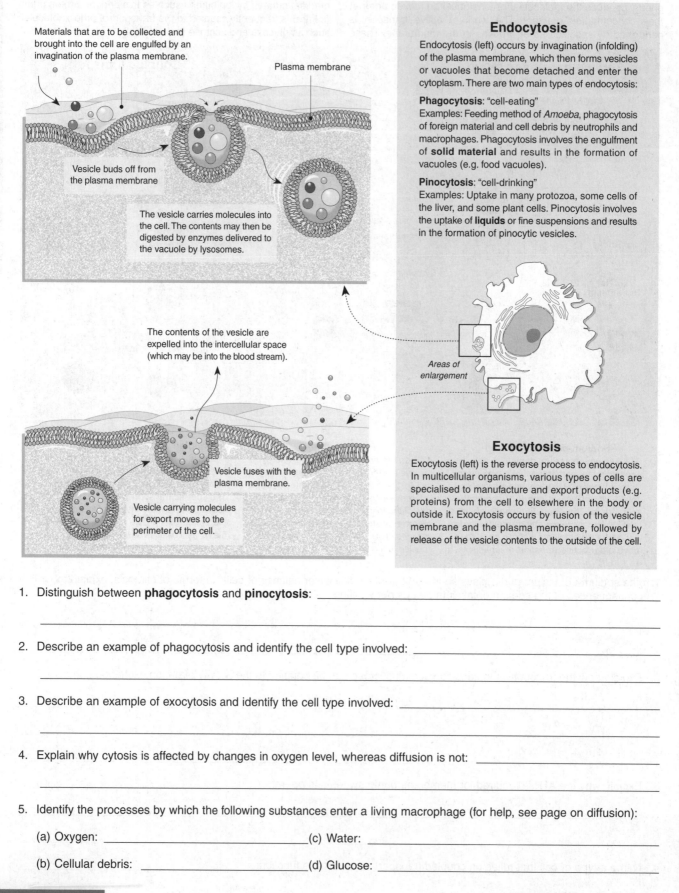

Materials that are to be collected and brought into the cell are engulfed by an invagination of the plasma membrane.

Plasma membrane

Vesicle buds off from the plasma membrane

The vesicle carries molecules into the cell. The contents may then be digested by enzymes delivered to the vacuole by lysosomes.

The contents of the vesicle are expelled into the intercellular space (which may be into the blood stream).

Vesicle fuses with the plasma membrane.

Vesicle carrying molecules for export moves to the perimeter of the cell.

Areas of enlargement

Endocytosis

Endocytosis (left) occurs by invagination (infolding) of the plasma membrane, which then forms vesicles or vacuoles that become detached and enter the cytoplasm. There are two main types of endocytosis:

Phagocytosis: "cell-eating"
Examples: Feeding method of *Amoeba*, phagocytosis of foreign material and cell debris by neutrophils and macrophages. Phagocytosis involves the engulfment of **solid material** and results in the formation of vacuoles (e.g. food vacuoles).

Pinocytosis: "cell-drinking"
Examples: Uptake in many protozoa, some cells of the liver, and some plant cells. Pinocytosis involves the uptake of **liquids** or fine suspensions and results in the formation of pinocytic vesicles.

Exocytosis

Exocytosis (left) is the reverse process to endocytosis. In multicellular organisms, various types of cells are specialised to manufacture and export products (e.g. proteins) from the cell to elsewhere in the body or outside it. Exocytosis occurs by fusion of the vesicle membrane and the plasma membrane, followed by release of the vesicle contents to the outside of the cell.

1. Distinguish between **phagocytosis** and **pinocytosis**: _____

   _____

2. Describe an example of phagocytosis and identify the cell type involved: _____

   _____

3. Describe an example of exocytosis and identify the cell type involved: _____

   _____

4. Explain why cytosis is affected by changes in oxygen level, whereas diffusion is not: _____

   _____

5. Identify the processes by which the following substances enter a living macrophage (for help, see page on diffusion):

   (a) Oxygen: _____ (c) Water: _____

   (b) Cellular debris: _____ (d) Glucose: _____

Cellular Energetics

Investigating energy requirements in the cell

The universal role of ATP in metabolism, for example in cellular respiration and photosynthesis.

Learning Objectives

☐ 1. Compile your own glossary from the **KEY WORDS** displayed in **bold type** in the learning objectives below.

The Role of ATP *(pages 75-76)*

☐ 2. Explain the need for energy in living things and the universal role of ATP in metabolism, as illustrated by specific examples e.g. **glycolysis**, **active transport**, **anabolic reactions**, movement, and **thermoregulation**.

☐ 3. Describe the structure of **ATP** as a phosphorylated nucleotide. Describe its synthesis from ADP and inorganic phosphate and explain how it stores and releases its energy.

☐ 4. Outline the principles involved in **photosynthesis** and **cellular respiration**, explaining in which way the two processes can be considered opposites.

☐ 5. Appreciate that both photosynthesis and cellular respiration involve the molecule **ATP** and a hydrogen carrier molecule (**$NADPH_2$** in photosynthesis, and **$NADH_2$** in respiration).

Cellular Respiration

Introduction to respiration *(pages 75-77)*

☐ 6. Describe the role of mitochondria in cellular respiration. Draw and label the structure of a **mitochondrion**, including the **matrix**, the outer and inner membrane and the **cristae**. Briefly state the function of each.

☐ 7. Identify the main steps in cellular respiration: **glycolysis**, **Krebs cycle** (*tricarboxylic acid cycle*) **electron transport system** (*electron transport chain, ETS, or respiratory chain*). On a diagram of a mitochondrion, indicate where each stage occurs. Recognise glycolysis as first stage in cellular respiration and the major anaerobic pathway in cells.

☐ 8. Identify **glucose** as the main respiratory substrate. Appreciate that other substrates can, through conversion, act as substrates for cellular respiration.

☐ 9. Outline **glycolysis** as the phosphorylation of glucose and the subsequent splitting of a 6C sugar into two triose phosphate molecules (2 X **pyruvate**). State the net yield of ATP and $NADH_2$ from glycolysis and appreciate that the subsequent metabolism of pyruvate depends on the availability of oxygen.

Aerobic respiration *(pages 79-80)*

☐ 10. Describe the complete oxidation of glucose to CO_2, with reference to:
- The conversion of pyruvate to **acetyl-coenzyme A**.
- The entry of acetyl CoA into the Krebs cycle by combination with **oxaloacetate**.

- The **Krebs cycle** (as a series of oxidation reactions involving release of CO_2, the production of $NAD.H_2$ or $FAD.H_2$, and the regeneration of oxaloacetate).
- The *role* of the coenzymes NAD and FAD.
- Synthesis of **ATP** by **oxidative phosphorylation** in the electron transport chain.
- The role of oxygen as the terminal electron acceptor and the formation of water.
- The net yield of ATP from aerobic respiration compared to the yield from glycolysis.

☐ 11. Explain oxidative phosphorylation in terms of **chemiosmosis** (the coupling of electron transport and the movement of hydrogen ions to the synthesis of ATP). Identify the role of the **electron carriers** and **ATP synthetase** (ATPase) in this process.

☐ 12. Understand the terms **decarboxylation** and **dehydrogenation** as they relate to the Krebs cycle.

Fermentation *(page 81)*

☐ 13. Understand the situations in which the pyruvate formed in glycolysis may not undergo complete oxidation. Describe the following examples of **fermentation**, identifying the H+ acceptor to each case:

(a) Formation of **lactic acid** in muscle.
(b) Formation of **ethanol** in yeast.

NOTE: Appreciate that, although fermentation is often used synonymously with anaerobic respiration, they are not the same. Respiration always involves hydrogen ions passing down a chain of carriers to a terminal acceptor, and this does not occur in fermentation. In anaerobic respiration, the terminal H+ acceptor is a molecule other than oxygen, e.g. Fe^{2+} or nitrate.

☐ 14. Compare and explain the differences in the yields of ATP from aerobic respiration and from fermentation.

Respiratory quotients *(page 78)*

☐ 15. Explain the relative energy values of carbohydrate, lipid, and protein as respiratory substrates. Explain the term **respiratory quotient** (RQ). Explain what RQ reveals about the substrate being respired.

☐ 16. Use a simple respirometer to measure RQ and the effect of temperature on respiration rate.

Photosynthesis

☐ 17. Appreciate that our current knowledge of photosynthesis can be traced to investigations of trained and lay scientists over more than 300 years.

Chloroplasts *(pages 82, 85)*

☐ 18. Describe the structure and role of **chloroplasts**, identifying the **stroma**, **grana**, lamellae (**thylakoids**), and location of the chlorophylls and other pigments.

19. Describe the role of **chlorophyll *a*** and ***b***, and **accessory pigments** (e.g. carotenoids) in light capture. Outline the differences in absorption of red, green, and blue light by chlorophyll.

20. In more detail than in #19 above, describe the absorption of light by **chlorophyll *a*** and ***b***, and **accessory pigments**. In particular, explain what is meant by the terms **absorption spectrum** and **action spectrum** with respect to the light absorbing pigments.

21. Investigate chloroplast pigments using chromatography.

Photosynthesis in C₃ plants *(pages 83-84)*

22. Describe, using diagrams, the reactions of photosynthesis in a C₃ plant with reference to:

23. The ***light dependent phase*** *(LDP)* with reference to:
   - Where in the chloroplast the LDP occurs.
   - The generation of ATP and $NADPH_2$ for use in the light independent phase.

24. In more detail than in #23 above describe the light dependent phase (LDP) with reference to:
   - The location and role of the photosystems.
   - The **photoactivation** of chlorophyll.
   - The splitting of water (**photolysis**) to produce protons and electrons.
   - The production of O_2 as a result of photolysis.
   - The transfer of energy to ATP (photophosphorylation) and the formation of $NADPH_2$ (reduced NADP).

25. In greater detail than in #24 above, explain photophosphorylation in terms of **chemiosmosis** (the coupling of electron transport and the movement of hydrogen ions to the synthesis of ATP). Relate the accumulation of H^+ inside the thylakoid to the generation of ATP by **ATP synthetase** (ATPase).

26. Distinguish between cyclic and non-cyclic (photo) phosphorylation:

- **Cyclic photophosphorylation**: electrons leaving photosystem I return to photosystem I with the generation of ATP but no $NADPH_2$.
- **Non-cyclic photophosphorylation**: electrons leaving photosystem I are replaced by the photolysis of water by photosystem II with the generation of ATP and $NADPH_2$. This normal flow of electrons is linear from photosystem II to photosystem I.

27. The ***light independent phase*** *(LIP)* with reference to:
   - Where in the chloroplast the LIP occurs.
   - The **Calvin cycle** and the fixation of carbon dioxide using ATP and $NADPH_2$ generated in the light dependent phase.

28. In more detail than in #27 above describe the light independent phase (LIP) with reference to the **Calvin cycle** including the following:
   - The fixation of carbon dioxide into a 5C compound, **ribulose bisphosphate** (RuBP).
   - The reduction of **glycerate-3-phosphate** (PGA) to **carbohydrate** and the role of **ATP** and **$NADPH_2$** (formed in the light dependent phase) in this.
   - The regeneration of the ribulose bisphosphate.

Photosynthesis in C₄ plants *(page 87)*

29. With respect to photosynthesis, describe the adaptations of C_4 plants. Emphasis the adaptive value of the C_4 pathway in providing a way to fix CO_2 at low concentrations as a 4C acid (**malate**) and use this to boost CO_2 levels for carbon fixation in the Calvin cycle.

Photosynthetic rate *(page 86)*

30. Understand the term **photosynthetic rate**. With reference to **limiting factors**, describe the effect of each of the following on photosynthetic rate:
   - Light intensity and wavelength
   - Temperature
   - Carbon dioxide concentration

See page 7 for additional details of this text:

■ Tobin, A.J. and Morel, R.E., 1997. **Asking About Cells**, (Thomson Brooks/Cole), part II.

See page 7 for details of publishers of periodicals:

STUDENT'S REFERENCE

Chlorophyll and photosynthesis

■ **Growing Plants in the Perfect Environment** Biol. Sci. Rev., 15(2) November 2002, pp. 12-16. *To manipulate the growth of plants in controlled environments, one must understand how plants grow and what influences photosynthetic rate.*

■ **Photosynthesis....Most hated Topic?** Biol. Sci. Rev., 20(1) Sept. 200, pp. 13-16. *A useful account documenting key points when learning about processes in photosynthesis.*

■ **Chemistry that Comes Naturally** New Scientist, 31 July 1993, pp. 24-28. *The processes of photosynthesis and respiration.*

■ **Green Miracle** New Scientist, 14 August 1999, pp. 26-30. *The mechanism by which plants split water to make oxygen remains a mystery.*

■ **Chlorophyll** Biol. Sci. Rev., 8(3) January 1996, pp. 28-30. *The chlorophyll molecule: how it absorbs light and its role in photosynthesis.*

■ **Why Don't Plants Wear Sunhats?** Biol. Sci. Rev., 9(3) Jan. 1997, pp. 32-35. *Plants need light, but too much is damaging - how do they cope?*

ATP and cellular respiration

■ **Fat Burns in the Flame of Carbohydrate** Biol. Sci. Rev., 15(3) February 2003, pp. 37-41. *A thorough account of both carbohydrate metabolism and how fatty acid oxidation feeds into the Krebs cycle. Starvation and ketosis are described and several points for discussion are included.*

■ **The Role of ATP in Cells** Biol. Sci. Rev., 19(2) Nov. 2006, pp. 30-33. *Synthesis and uses of ATP.*

■ **Fuelled for Life** New Scientist, 13 January 1996 (Inside Science). *Energy and metabolism: ATP, glycolysis, electron transport system, Krebs cycle, and enzymes and cofactors.*

■ **Glucose Catabolism** Biol. Sci. Rev., 10(3) Jan. 1998, pp. 22-24. *Glucose in cells: oxidative phosphorylation and the role of mitochondria.*

TEACHER'S REFERENCE

■ **Measuring the Metabolism of Small Organisms** Scientific American, December 1995, pp. 84-85. *Methods of measuring and monitoring respiration and metabolic rate in small organisms.*

■ **Learn about Cellular Respiration** The American Biology Teacher, 60(9) Nov. 1998, pp. 681-683. *Ideas on how to explore the concepts relating to cellular respiration.*

■ **Simple Inexpensive Respirometers & Demonstrations Where Plants do the Unexpected: Give off Carbon Dioxide!** The Am. Biology Teacher, 68(5) May 2006, pp. 293-295. *Students design experiments to measure plant respiration inside plastic pipettes.*

■ **The Photosynthetic Dark Reactions do not Operate in the Dark** The American Biology Teacher, 62(3) March 2000, pp. 166-170. *This account explores the misconception that the*

'dark' reactions occur in the dark: some of the the enzymes are indirectly dependent on the light.

■ **Green Miracle** New Scientist, 14 August 1999, pp. 26-30. *The mechanism by which plants split water to make oxygen remains a mystery.*

See pages 4-5 for details of how to access **Bio Links** from our web site: **www.thebiozone.com** From Bio Links, access sites under the topics:

GENERAL BIOLOGY ONLINE RESOURCES > Online Textbooks and Lecture Notes: • S-Cool! A level biology revision guide • Learn.co.uk • Mark Rothery's biology web site ... *and others*

CELL BIOLOGY AND BIOCHEMISTRY: • Cell and molecular biology online ... *and others >* **Biochemistry and Metabolic Pathways:** • Calvin cycle (C3 cycle) • Cellular energy references • Cellular respiration • Cycle (Krebs cycle, Citric Acid Cycle) • Electron transport chain • Energy, enzymes, and catalysis problem set • Glycolysis • Learning about photosynthesis • Chapter 7: Metabolism and biochemistry ... *and others*

Presentation MEDIA to support this topic:

Cell Biology & Biochemistry

CELL BIO & BIOCHEM
• **Cellular Energetics**

Energy in Cells

A summary of the flow of energy within a plant cell is illustrated below. Animal cells have a similar flow except the glucose is supplied by ingestion rather than by photosynthesis. The energy not immediately stored in chemical bonds is lost as heat. Note the role of ATP; it is made in cellular respiration and provides the energy for metabolic reactions, including photosynthesis.

Energy Transformations in a Photosynthetic Plant Cell

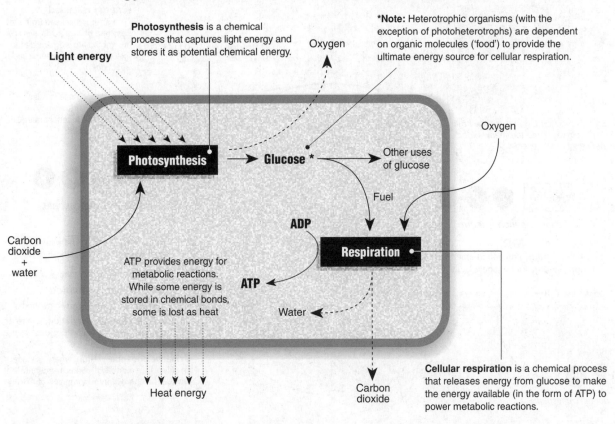

Photosynthesis is a chemical process that captures light energy and stores it as potential chemical energy.

*Note: Heterotrophic organisms (with the exception of photoheterotrophs) are dependent on organic molecules ('food') to provide the ultimate energy source for cellular respiration.

ATP provides energy for metabolic reactions. While some energy is stored in chemical bonds, some is lost as heat

Cellular respiration is a chemical process that releases energy from glucose to make the energy available (in the form of ATP) to power metabolic reactions.

Cellular Energetics

1. Distinguish between **heterotrophs**, **photosynthetic autotrophs**, and **chemosynthetic autotrophs** with respect to how these organisms derive their source of energy for metabolism:

_____

_____

_____

_____

_____

_____

2. In 1977, scientists working near the Galapagos Islands in the equatorial eastern Pacific found warm water spewing from cracks in the mid-oceanic ridges 2600 metres below the surface. Clustered around these hydrothermal vents were strange and beautiful creatures new to science. The entire community depends on sulfur-oxidising bacteria that use hydrogen sulfide dissolved in the venting water as an energy source to manufacture carbohydrates. This process is similar to photosynthesis, but does not rely on sunlight to provide the energy for generating ATP and fixing carbon:

(a) Explain why a community based on photosynthetic organisms is not found at this site: _____

_____

(b) Name the ultimate energy source for the bacteria: _____

(c) This same chemical that provides the bacteria with energy is also toxic to the process of cellular respiration; a problem that the animals living in the habitat have resolved by evolving various adaptations. Explain what would happen if these animals did not possess adaptations to reduce the toxic effect on cellular respiration:

_____

(d) Name the energy source classification for these sulfur-oxidising bacteria: _____

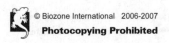

Code: RA 2

The Role of ATP in Cells

The molecule ATP (adenosine triphosphate) is the universal energy carrier for the cell. ATP can release its energy quickly; only one chemical reaction (hydrolysis of the terminal phosphate) is required. This reaction is catalysed by the enzyme ATPase. Once ATP has released its energy, it becomes ADP (adenosine diphosphate), a low energy molecule that can be recharged by adding a phosphate. This requires energy, which is supplied by the controlled breakdown of respiratory substrates in cellular respiration. The most common respiratory substrate is glucose, but other molecules (e.g. fats or proteins) may also be used.

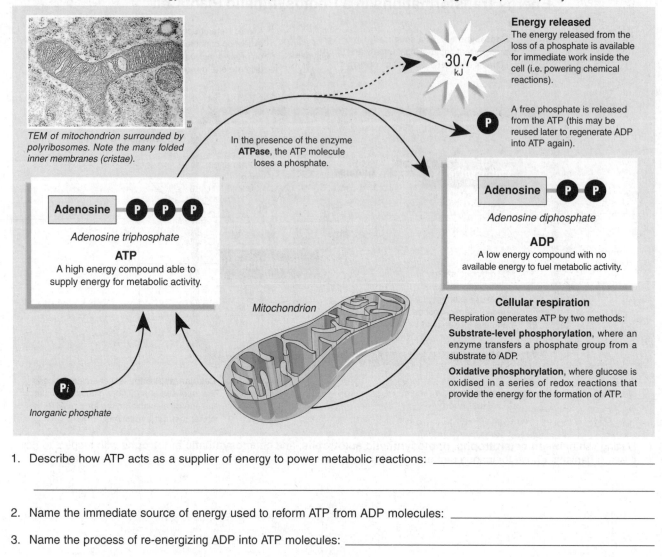

TEM of mitochondrion surrounded by polyribosomes. Note the many folded inner membranes (cristae).

In the presence of the enzyme **ATPase**, the ATP molecule loses a phosphate.

Energy released
The energy released from the loss of a phosphate is available for immediate work inside the cell (i.e. powering chemical reactions).

30.7 kJ

A free phosphate is released from the ATP (this may be reused later to regenerate ADP into ATP again).

Adenosine P P P

Adenosine triphosphate
ATP
A high energy compound able to supply energy for metabolic activity.

Adenosine P P

Adenosine diphosphate
ADP
A low energy compound with no available energy to fuel metabolic activity.

Mitochondrion

Pi
Inorganic phosphate

Cellular respiration
Respiration generates ATP by two methods:

Substrate-level phosphorylation, where an enzyme transfers a phosphate group from a substrate to ADP.

Oxidative phosphorylation, where glucose is oxidised in a series of redox reactions that provide the energy for the formation of ATP.

1. Describe how ATP acts as a supplier of energy to power metabolic reactions: _____

_____

2. Name the immediate source of energy used to reform ATP from ADP molecules: _____

3. Name the process of re-energizing ADP into ATP molecules: _____

4. Name the ultimate source of energy for plants: _____

5. Name the ultimate source of energy for animals: _____

6. Explain in what way the ADP/ATP system can be likened to a rechargeable battery: _____

_____

7. In the following table, use brief statements to contrast photosynthesis and respiration in terms of the following:

Feature	Photosynthesis	Cellular respiration
Starting materials		
Waste products		
Role of hydrogen carriers: NAD, NADP		
Role of ATP		
Overall biological role		

Cellular Respiration

Cellular respiration is the process by which organisms break down energy rich molecules (e.g. glucose) to release the energy in a useable form (ATP). All living cells respire in order to exist, although the substrates they use may vary. **Aerobic respiration** requires oxygen. Forms of cellular respiration that do not require oxygen are said to be **anaerobic**. Some plants and animals can generate ATP anaerobically for short periods of time. Other organisms use only anaerobic respiration and live in oxygen-free environments. For these organisms, there is some other final electron acceptor other than oxygen (e.g. nitrate or Fe^{2+}).

An Overview of Cellular Respiration

Respiration involves three metabolic stages, summarised below. The first two stages are the catabolic pathways that decompose glucose and other organic fuels. In the third stage, the electron transport chain accepts electrons from the first two stages and passes these from one electron acceptor to another. The energy released at each stepwise transfer is used to make ATP. The final electron acceptor in this process is molecular oxygen.

1. **Glycolysis**. This occurs in the cytoplasm and involves the breakdown of glucose into two molecules of pyruvate.

2. **The Krebs cycle**. This occurs in the mitochondrial matrix, and decomposes a derivative of pyruvate to carbon dioxide.

3. **Electron transport and oxidative phosphorylation**. This occurs in the inner membranes of the mitochondrion and accounts for almost 90% of the ATP generated by respiration.

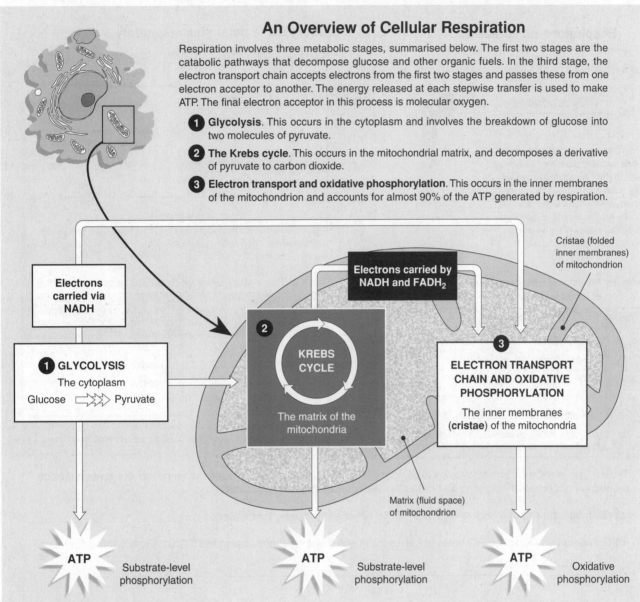

Cellular Energetics

1. Describe precisely in which part of the cell the following take place:

   (a) Glycolysis: _____

   (b) Krebs cycle reactions: _____

   (c) Electron transport chain: _____

2. Provide a clear explanation of what is involved in each of the following processes:

   (a) Substrate-level phosphorylation: _____

   _____

   _____

   (b) Oxidative phosphorylation: _____

   _____

   _____

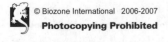

Code: RA 1

Measuring Respiration

In small animals or germinating seeds, the rate of cellular respiration can be measured using a simple respirometer: a sealed unit where the carbon dioxide produced by the respiring tissues is absorbed by soda lime and the volume of oxygen consumed is detected by fluid displacement in a manometer. Germinating seeds are also often used to calculate the **respiratory quotient** (RQ): the ratio of the amount of carbon dioxide produced during cellular respiration to the amount of oxygen consumed. RQ provides a useful indication of the respiratory substrate being used.

Respiratory substrates and RQ

The respiratory quotient (RQ) can be expressed simply as:

$$RQ = \frac{CO_2 \text{ produced}}{O_2 \text{ consumed}}$$

When pure carbohydrate is oxidised in cellular respiration, the RQ is 1.0; more oxygen is required to oxidise fatty acids (RQ = 0.7). The RQ for protein is about 0.9. Organisms usually respire a mix of substrates, giving RQ values of between 0.8 and 0.9 (see table 1, below).

Table 1: RQ values for the respiration of various substrates

RQ	Substrate
> 1.0	Carbohydrate with some anaerobic respiration
1.0	Carbohydrates, e.g. glucose
0.9	Protein
0.7	Fat
0.5	Fat with associated carbohydrate synthesis
0.3	Carbohydrate with associated organic acid synthesis

Using RQ to determine respiratory substrate

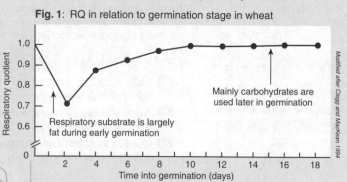

Fig. 1: RQ in relation to germination stage in wheat

Respiratory substrate is largely fat during early germination

Mainly carbohydrates are used later in germination

Time into germination (days)

Modified after Clegg and MacKean 1994

Fig. 1, above, shows how experimental RQ values have been used to determine the respiratory substrate utilised by germinating wheat seeds (*Triticum sativum*) over the period of their germination.

Table 2: Rates of O_2 consumption and CO_2 production in crickets

Time after last fed (h)	Temperature (°C)	Rate of O_2 consumption ($mlg^{-1}h^{-1}$)	Rate of CO_2 production ($mlg^{-1}h^{-1}$)
1	20	2.82	2.82
48	20	2.82	1.97
1	30	5.12	5.12
48	30	5.12	3.57

Table 2 shows the rates of oxygen consumption and carbon dioxide production of crickets kept under different experimental conditions.

1. Table 2 above shows the results of an experiment to measure the rates of oxygen consumption and carbon dioxide production of crickets 1 hour and 48 hours after feeding at different temperatures:

   (a) Calculate the RQ of a cricket kept at 20°C, 48 hours after feeding (show working): _____

   (b) Compare this RQ to the RQ value obtained for the cricket 1 hour after being fed (20°C). Explain the difference:

   _____

   _____

2. The RQs of two species of seeds were calculated at two day intervals after germination. Results are tabulated to the right:

   (a) Plot the change in RQ of the two species during early germination:

   (b) Explain the values in terms of the possible substrates being respired:

Days after germination	RQ	
	Seedling A	Seedling B
2	0.65	0.70
4	0.35	0.91
6	0.48	0.98
8	0.68	1.00
10	0.70	1.00

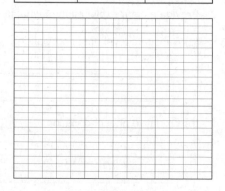

The Biochemistry of Respiration

Cellular respiration is a catabolic, energy yielding pathway. The breakdown of glucose and other organic fuels (such as fats and proteins) to simpler molecules is **exergonic** and releases energy for the synthesis of ATP. As summarised in the previous activity, respiration involves glycolysis, the Krebs cycle, and electron transport. The diagram below provides a more detailed overview of the events in each of these stages. Glycolysis and the Krebs cycle supply electrons (via NADH) to the electron transport chain, which drives **oxidative phosphorylation**. Glycolysis nets two ATP, produced by **substrate-level phosphorylation**.

The conversion of pyruvate (the end product of glycolysis) to **acetyl CoA** links glycolysis to the Krebs cycle. One "turn" of the cycle releases carbon dioxide, forms one ATP by substrate level phosphorylation, and passes electrons to three NAD^+ and one FAD. Most of the ATP generated in cellular respiration is produced by oxidative phosphorylation when NADH and $FADH_2$ donate electrons to the series of electron carriers in the electron transport chain. At the end of the chain, electrons are passed to molecular oxygen, reducing it to water. Electron transport is coupled to ATP synthesis by **chemiosmosis** (see next page).

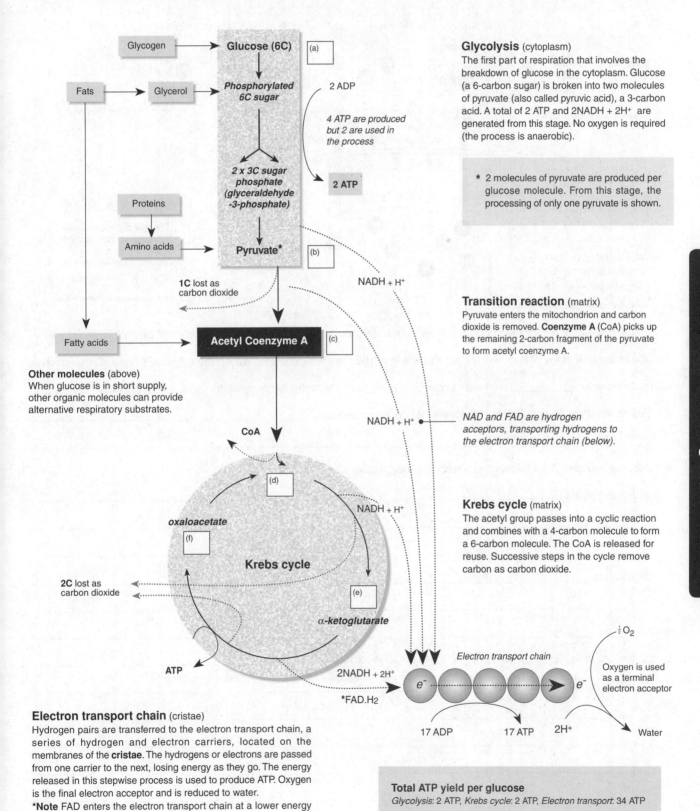

Glycolysis (cytoplasm)
The first part of respiration that involves the breakdown of glucose in the cytoplasm. Glucose (a 6-carbon sugar) is broken into two molecules of pyruvate (also called pyruvic acid), a 3-carbon acid. A total of 2 ATP and $2NADH + 2H^+$ are generated from this stage. No oxygen is required (the process is anaerobic).

* 2 molecules of pyruvate are produced per glucose molecule. From this stage, the processing of only one pyruvate is shown.

Transition reaction (matrix)
Pyruvate enters the mitochondrion and carbon dioxide is removed. **Coenzyme A** (CoA) picks up the remaining 2-carbon fragment of the pyruvate to form acetyl coenzyme A.

NAD and FAD are hydrogen acceptors, transporting hydrogens to the electron transport chain (below).

Krebs cycle (matrix)
The acetyl group passes into a cyclic reaction and combines with a 4-carbon molecule to form a 6-carbon molecule. The CoA is released for reuse. Successive steps in the cycle remove carbon as carbon dioxide.

Other molecules (above)
When glucose is in short supply, other organic molecules can provide alternative respiratory substrates.

Electron transport chain (cristae)
Hydrogen pairs are transferred to the electron transport chain, a series of hydrogen and electron carriers, located on the membranes of the **cristae**. The hydrogens or electrons are passed from one carrier to the next, losing energy as they go. The energy released in this stepwise process is used to produce ATP. Oxygen is the final electron acceptor and is reduced to water.
*Note FAD enters the electron transport chain at a lower energy level than NAD, and only 2ATP are generated per FAD.H2.

Total ATP yield per glucose
Glycolysis: 2 ATP, Krebs cycle: 2 ATP, Electron transport: 34 ATP

Cellular Energetics

Code: A 3

Chemiosmosis

Chemiosmosis is the process whereby the synthesis of ATP is coupled to electron transport and the movement of protons (H^+ ions). **Electron transport carriers** are arranged over the inner membrane of the mitochondrion and oxidise NADH + H^+ and $FADH_2$. Energy from this process forces protons to move, against their concentration gradient, from the mitochondrial matrix into the space between the two membranes. Eventually the protons flow back into the matrix via ATP synthetase molecules in the membrane. As the protons flow down their concentration gradient, energy is released and ATP is synthesised. Chemiosmotic theory also explains the generation of ATP in the light dependent phase of photosynthesis.

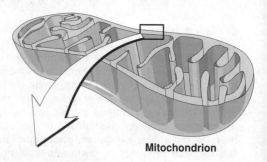

Mitochondrion

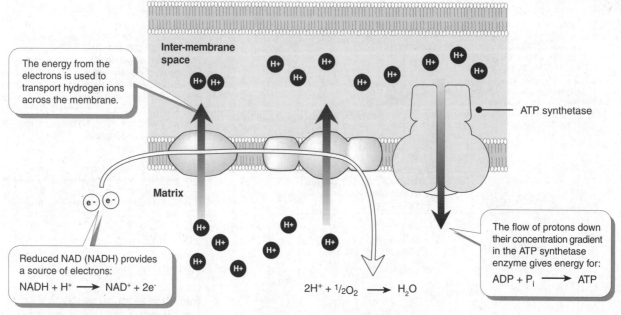

The energy from the electrons is used to transport hydrogen ions across the membrane.

Inter-membrane space

Matrix

ATP synthetase

Reduced NAD (NADH) provides a source of electrons:

$$NADH + H^+ \longrightarrow NAD^+ + 2e^-$$

$$2H^+ + \tfrac{1}{2}O_2 \longrightarrow H_2O$$

The flow of protons down their concentration gradient in the ATP synthetase enzyme gives energy for:

$$ADP + P_i \longrightarrow ATP$$

1. On the diagram of cellular respiration (previous page), state the number of carbon atoms in each of the molecules (a) – (f):

2. Determine how many ATP molecules **per molecule of glucose** are generated during the following stages of respiration:

   (a) Glycolysis: _____ (b) Krebs cycle: _____ (c) Electron transport chain: _____ (d) Total: _____

3. Explain what happens to the carbon atoms lost during respiration: _____

   _____

4. Describe the role of the following in aerobic cellular respiration:

   (a) Hydrogen atoms: _____

   _____

   _____

   (b) Oxygen: _____

   _____

   _____

5. (a) Identify the process by which ATP is synthesised in respiration: _____

   (b) Briefly summarise this process: _____

   _____

   _____

   _____

   _____

   _____

   _____

Anaerobic Pathways

All organisms can metabolise glucose anaerobically (without oxygen) using glycolysis in the cytoplasm, but the energy yield from this process is low and few organisms can obtain sufficient energy for their needs this way. In the absence of oxygen, glycolysis soon stops unless there is an alternative acceptor for the electrons produced from the glycolytic pathway. In yeasts and the root cells of higher plants this acceptor is ethanal, and the pathway is called alcoholic fermentation. In the skeletal muscle of mammals, the acceptor is pyruvate itself and the end product is lactic acid. In both cases, the duration of the fermentation is limited by the toxic effects of the organic compound produced. Although fermentation is often used synonymously with anaerobic respiration, they are not the same. Respiration always involves hydrogen ions passing down a chain of carriers to a terminal acceptor, and this does not occur in fermentation. In anaerobic respiration, the terminal H^+ acceptor is a molecule other than oxygen, e.g. Fe^{2+} or nitrate.

Alcoholic Fermentation

In alcoholic fermentation, the H^+ acceptor is ethanal which is reduced to ethanol with the release of CO_2. Yeasts respire aerobically when oxygen is available but can use alcoholic fermentation when it is not. At levels above 12-15%, the ethanol produced by alcoholic fermentation is toxic to the yeast cells and this limits their ability to use this pathway indefinitely. The root cells of plants also use fermentation as a pathway when oxygen is unavailable but the ethanol must be converted back to respiratory inter-mediates and respired aerobically.

Lactic Acid Fermentation

In the absence of oxygen, the skeletal muscle cells of mammals are able to continue using glycolysis for ATP production by reducing pyruvate to lactic acid (the H^+ acceptor is pyruvate itself). This process is called lactic acid fermentation. Lactic acid is toxic and this pathway cannot continue indefinitely. The lactic acid must be removed from the muscle and transported to the liver, where it is converted back to respiratory inter-mediates and respired aerobically.

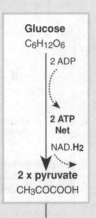

Glucose
$C_6H_{12}O_6$
2 ADP
2 ATP Net
NAD.H_2
2 x pyruvate
$CH_3COCOOH$

Glucose
$C_6H_{12}O_6$
2 ADP
2 ATP Net
NAD.H_2
2 x pyruvate
$CH_3COCOOH$

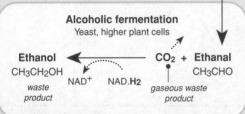

Alcoholic fermentation
Yeast, higher plant cells

Ethanol
CH_3CH_2OH
waste product
NAD$^+$ NAD.H_2
CO_2 + **Ethanal**
CH_3CHO
gaseous waste product

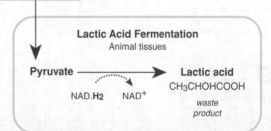

Lactic Acid Fermentation
Animal tissues

Pyruvate
NAD.H_2 NAD$^+$
Lactic acid
$CH_3CHOHCOOH$
waste product

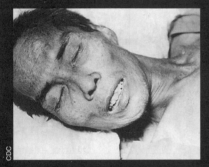

Some organisms respire only in the absence of oxygen and are known as **obligate anaerobes**. Many of these organisms are bacterial pathogens and cause diseases such as tetanus (*above*), gangrene, and botulism.

Vertebrate skeletal muscle is **facultatively anaerobic** because it has the ability to generate ATP for a short time in the absence of oxygen. The energy from this pathway comes from glycolysis and the yield is low.

The products of alcoholic fermentation have been utilised by humans for centuries. The alcohol and carbon dioxide produced from this process form the basis of the brewing and baking industries.

Cellular Energetics

1. Describe the key difference between aerobic respiration and fermentation: _____

_____

2. (a) Refer to page 30 and determine the efficiency of fermentation compared to aerobic respiration: _____ %

   (b) In simple terms, explain why the efficiency of anaerobic pathways is so low: _____

   _____

3. Explain why fermentation cannot go on indefinitely: _____

_____

_____

Code: RDA 2

Photosynthesis

Photosynthesis is of fundamental importance to living things because it transforms sunlight energy into chemical energy stored in molecules. This becomes part of the energy available in food chains. The molecules that trap the energy in their chemical bonds are also used as building blocks to create other molecules. Finally, photosynthesis releases free oxygen gas, essential for the survival of advanced life forms. Below is a diagram summarising the process of photosynthesis.

Summary of Photosynthesis in a C$_3$ Plant

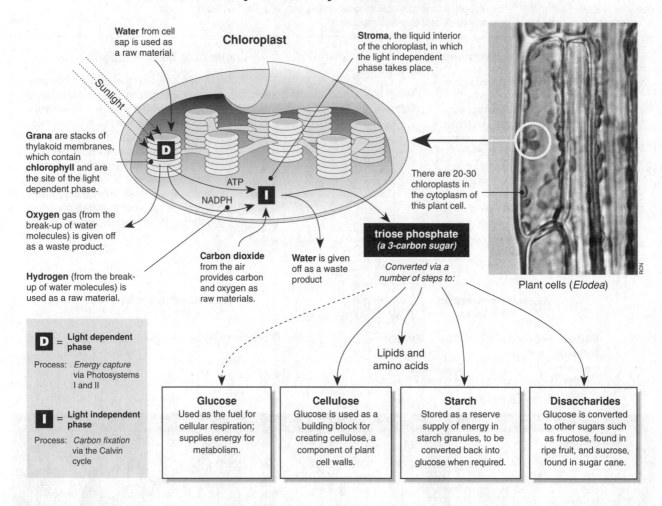

Water from cell sap is used as a raw material.

Chloroplast

Stroma, the liquid interior of the chloroplast, in which the light independent phase takes place.

Sunlight

Grana are stacks of thylakoid membranes, which contain **chlorophyll** and are the site of the light dependent phase.

D

ATP

NADPH

I

There are 20-30 chloroplasts in the cytoplasm of this plant cell.

Oxygen gas (from the break-up of water molecules) is given off as a waste product.

Hydrogen (from the break-up of water molecules) is used as a raw material.

Carbon dioxide from the air provides carbon and oxygen as raw materials.

Water is given off as a waste product

triose phosphate *(a 3-carbon sugar)*

Converted via a number of steps to:

Plant cells (*Elodea*)

D = **Light dependent phase**

Process: *Energy capture via Photosystems I and II*

I = **Light independent phase**

Process: *Carbon fixation via the Calvin cycle*

Lipids and amino acids

Glucose
Used as the fuel for cellular respiration; supplies energy for metabolism.

Cellulose
Glucose is used as a building block for creating cellulose, a component of plant cell walls.

Starch
Stored as a reserve supply of energy in starch granules, to be converted back into glucose when required.

Disaccharides
Glucose is converted to other sugars such as fructose, found in ripe fruit, and sucrose, found in sugar cane.

1. Describe the three things of fundamental biological importance provided by photosynthesis:

   (a) _____

   (b) _____

   (c) _____

2. Write the overall chemical equation for photosynthesis using:

   (a) Words: _____

   (b) Chemical symbols: _____

3. Discuss the potential uses for the end products of photosynthesis: _____

   _____

   _____

4. Distinguish between the two different regions of a chloroplast and describe the biochemical processes that occur in each:

   _____

   _____

   _____

The Biochemistry of Photosynthesis

Like cellular respiration, photosynthesis is a redox process, but the electron flow evident in respiration is reversed. In photosynthesis, water is split and electrons are transferred together with hydrogen ions from water to CO_2, reducing it to sugar. The electrons increase in potential energy as they move from water to sugar. The energy to do this is provided by light. Photosynthesis comprises two phases. In the **light**

dependent phase, light energy is converted to chemical energy (ATP and reducing power). In the **light independent phase** (or **Calvin cycle**), the chemical energy is used for the synthesis of carbohydrate. The light dependent phase illustrated below shows **non-cyclic phosphorylation**. In **cyclic phosphorylation**, the electrons lost from photosystem II are replaced by those from photosystem I. ATP is generated, but not NADPH.

Light Dependent Phase
(Energy capture)

- This diagram shows **non-cyclic phosphorylation**.

- Photosystem complexes comprise hundreds of pigment molecules, including *chlorophyll a* and *b*.

- **Photosystem II** absorbs light energy to elevate electrons to a moderate energy level.

- **Photosystem I** absorbs light energy to elevate electrons to an even higher level. Its electrons are replaced by electrons from photosystem II.

Chloroplast

Water

Stroma

Grana are stacks of thylakoid membranes *(enlarged below)*

| **D** | Light dependent |
| **I** | Light independent |

Oxygen

Hydrogen

ATP

NADPH

Carbon dioxide

Water

triose phosphate

Electron transport chain: Each electron is passed from one electron carrier to another, losing energy as it goes. This energy is used to pump hydrogen ions across the thylakoid membrane.

When chlorophyll molecules absorb light, an electron is excited to a higher level. This electron 'hole' must be filled.

Detail of Thylakoid Membrane

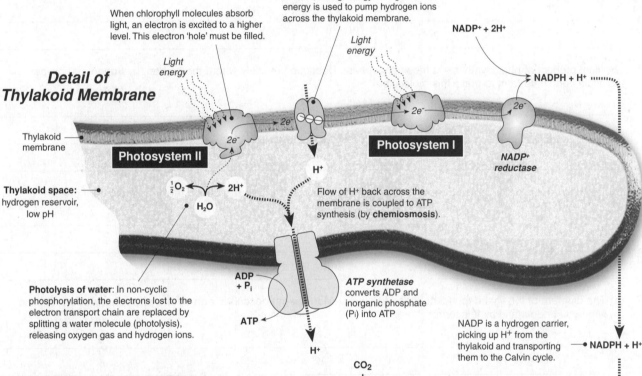

Light energy

Light energy

$NADP^+ + 2H^+$

$NADPH + H^+$

Thylakoid membrane

$2e^-$

$2e^-$

$2e^-$

$2e^-$

Photosystem II

Photosystem I

NADP$^+$ reductase

Thylakoid space: hydrogen reservoir, low pH

$\frac{1}{2}O_2$ $2H^+$

H_2O

H^+

Flow of H^+ back across the membrane is coupled to ATP synthesis (by **chemiosmosis**).

Photolysis of water: In non-cyclic phosphorylation, the electrons lost to the electron transport chain are replaced by splitting a water molecule (photolysis), releasing oxygen gas and hydrogen ions.

ADP + P$_i$

ATP synthetase converts ADP and inorganic phosphate (P$_i$) into ATP

ATP

H^+

NADP is a hydrogen carrier, picking up H^+ from the thylakoid and transporting them to the Calvin cycle.

$NADPH + H^+$

CO_2

Light Independent Phase
(Carbon fixation)

The light independent reaction, called the **Calvin cycle**, has also been labelled the 'dark phase' of photosynthesis. This is not a good label as it is not necessary that the phase occur in darkness; it simply does not require light to proceed. In the Calvin cycle, hydrogen (H^+) is added to CO_2 and a 5C intermediate to make carbohydrate. The H^+ and ATP are supplied by the light dependent phase above.

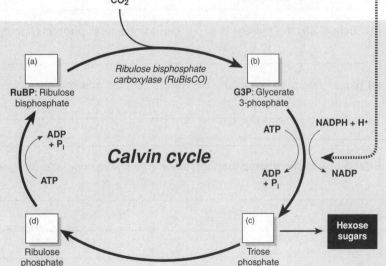

(a)

RuBP: Ribulose bisphosphate

Ribulose bisphosphate carboxylase (RuBisCO)

(b)

G3P: Glycerate 3-phosphate

$NADPH + H^+$

ATP

ADP + P$_i$

ADP + P$_i$

ATP

NADP

Calvin cycle

(d)

Ribulose phosphate

(c)

Triose phosphate

Hexose sugars

Cellular Energetics

Code: RA 3

1. Describe the role of the carrier molecule **NADP** in photosynthesis: _____

_____

_____

2. Explain the role of chlorophyll molecules in the process of photosynthesis: _____

_____

_____

_____

3. On the diagram on the previous page, write the number of carbon atoms that each molecule has at each stage of the Calvin cycle:

4. Summarise the events in each of the two phases in photosynthesis and identify where each phase occurs:

    (a) **Light dependent phase (D)**: _____

    _____

    _____

    (b) **Calvin cycle**: _____

    _____

    _____

5. The final product of photosynthesis is triose phosphate. Describe precisely where the carbon, hydrogen and oxygen molecules originate from to make this molecule:

_____

_____

_____

6. Explain how ATP is produced as a result of light striking chlorophyll molecules during the light dependent phase:

_____

_____

_____

7. (a) The diagram of the light dependent phase (on the previous page) describes **non-cyclic phosphorylation**. Explain what you understand by this term:

    _____

    _____

    (b) Suggest why this process is also known as non-cyclic **photo**phosphorylation: _____

    _____

    (c) Explain how photophosphorylation differs from the oxidative phosphorylation occurring in cellular respiration:

    _____

    _____

8. Explain how **cyclic photophosphorylation** differs from non-cyclic photophosphorylation: _____

_____

_____

_____

_____

Pigments and Light Absorption

As light meets matter, it may be reflected, transmitted, or absorbed. Substances that absorb visible light are called **pigments**, and different pigments absorb light of different wavelengths. The ability of a pigment to absorb particular wavelengths of light can be measured with a spectrophotometer. The light absorption vs the wavelength is called the **absorption spectrum** of that pigment. The absorption spectrum of different photosynthetic pigments provides clues to their role in photosynthesis, since light can only perform work if it is absorbed. An **action spectrum** profiles the effectiveness of different wavelength light in fuelling photosynthesis. It is obtained by plotting wavelength against some measure of photosynthetic rate (e.g. CO_2 production). Some features of photosynthetic pigments and their light absorbing properties are outlined below.

The Electromagnetic Spectrum

Light is a form of energy known as electromagnetic radiation. The segment of the electromagnetic spectrum most important to life is the narrow band between about 380 and 750 nanometres (nm). This radiation is known as visible light because it is detected as colours by the human eye (although some other animals, such as insects, can see in the ultraviolet range). It is the visible light that drives photosynthesis.

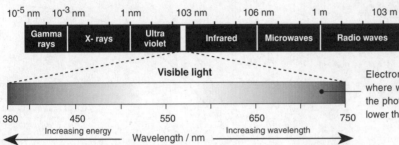

Electromagnetic radiation (EMR) travels in waves, where wavelength provides a guide to the energy of the photons; the greater the wavelength of EMR, the lower the energy of the photons in that radiation.

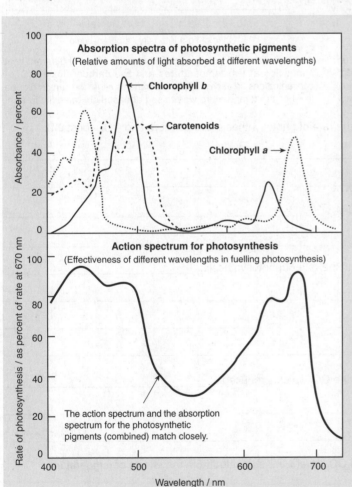

The Photosynthetic Pigments of Plants

The photosynthetic pigments of plants fall into two categories: **chlorophylls** (which absorb red and blue-violet light) and **carotenoids** (which absorb strongly in the blue-violet and appear orange, yellow, or red). The pigments are located on the chloroplast membranes (the thylakoids) and are associated with membrane transport systems.

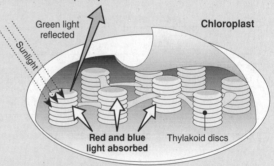

The pigments of chloroplasts in higher plants (above) absorb blue and red light, and the leaves therefore appear green (which is reflected). Each photosynthetic pigment has its own characteristic **absorption spectrum** (left, top graph). Although only chlorophyll *a* can participate directly in the light reactions of photosynthesis, the **accessory pigments** (chlorophyll *b* and carotenoids) can absorb wavelengths of light that chlorophyll *a* cannot. The accessory pigments pass the energy (photons) to chlorophyll *a*, thus broadening the spectrum that can effectively drive photosynthesis.

Left: Graphs comparing absorption spectra of photosynthetic pigments compared with the action spectrum for photosynthesis.

Cellular Energetics

1. Explain what is meant by the absorption spectrum of a pigment: _____

_____

2. Explain why the action spectrum for photosynthesis does not exactly match the absorption spectrum of chlorophyll *a*:

_____

_____

Code: A 2

Photosynthetic Rate

The rate at which plants can make food (the photosynthetic rate) is dependent on environmental factors, particularly the amount of **light** available, the level of **carbon dioxide** (CO_2) and the **temperature**. The effect of these factors can be tested experimentally by altering one of the factors while holding others constant (a controlled experiment). In reality, a plant is subjected to variations in all three factors at the same time. The interaction of the different factors can also be examined in the same way, as long as only one factor at a time is altered. The results can be expressed graphically.

Factors Affecting Photosynthetic Rate

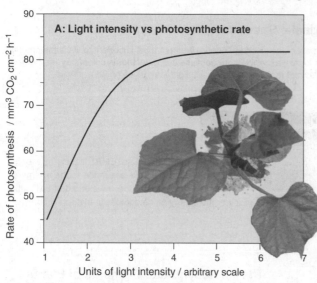

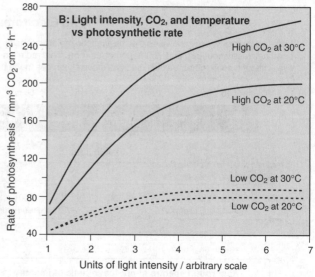

The two graphs above illustrate the effect of different variables on the rate of photosynthesis in cucumber plants. Graph A (above, left) shows the effect of different intensities of light. In this experiment, the level of carbon dioxide available and the temperature were kept constant. Graph B (above, right) shows the effect of different light intensities at two temperatures and two carbon dioxide (CO_2) concentrations. In each of these experiments either the carbon dioxide level or the temperature was raised at each light intensity in turn.

1. (a) Describe the effect of increasing light intensity on the rate of photosynthesis (temperature and CO_2 constant):

_____

_____

   (b) Give a possible explanation for the shape of the curve: _____

_____

2. (a) Describe the effect of increasing the temperature on the rate of photosynthesis: _____

_____

   (b) Suggest a reason for this response: _____

_____

3. Explain why the rate of photosynthesis declines when the CO_2 level is reduced: _____

_____

_____

4. (a) In the graph above right, explain how the effects of CO_2 level were separated from the effects of temperature:

_____

_____

   (b) State which of the two factors, CO_2 level or temperature, has the greatest effect on photosynthetic rate:

_____

   (c) Explain how you can tell this from the graph: _____

_____

Code: DA 2

Photosynthesis in C₄ Plants

When photosynthesis takes place, the first detectable compound which is made by a plant is usually a 3-carbon compound called GP (glycerate 3-phosphate). Plants which do this are called C₃ plants. In some plants, however, a 4-carbon molecule called oxaloacetate, is the first to be made. Such plants, which include cereals and tropical grasses, are called C₄ plants. These plants have a high rate of photosynthesis, thriving in environments with high light levels and warm temperatures. Their yield of photosynthetic products is higher than that of C₃ plants, giving them a competitive advantage in tropical climates. The high productivity of the C₄ system is also an important property of crop plants such as sugar cane and maize.

Structure of a Leaf from a C₄ Plant

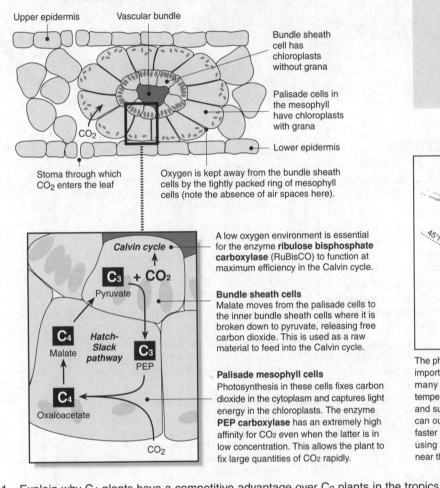

Upper epidermis   Vascular bundle

Bundle sheath cell has chloroplasts without grana

Palisade cells in the mesophyll have chloroplasts with grana

Lower epidermis

CO₂

Stoma through which CO₂ enters the leaf

Oxygen is kept away from the bundle sheath cells by the tightly packed ring of mesophyll cells (note the absence of air spaces here).

Calvin cycle •

C₃ + CO₂

Pyruvate

C₄   Hatch-Slack pathway   C₃
Malate   PEP

C₄
Oxaloacetate

CO₂

A low oxygen environment is essential for the enzyme **ribulose bisphosphate carboxylase** (RuBisCO) to function at maximum efficiency in the Calvin cycle.

Bundle sheath cells
Malate moves from the palisade cells to the inner bundle sheath cells where it is broken down to pyruvate, releasing free carbon dioxide. This is used as a raw material to feed into the Calvin cycle.

Palisade mesophyll cells
Photosynthesis in these cells fixes carbon dioxide in the cytoplasm and captures light energy in the chloroplasts. The enzyme **PEP carboxylase** has an extremely high affinity for CO₂ even when the latter is in low concentration. This allows the plant to fix large quantities of CO₂ rapidly.

Examples of C₄ plants
- Sugar cane *(Saccharum officinale)*
- Maize *(Zea mays)*
- Sorghum *(Sorghum bicolor)*
- Sun plant *(Portulaca grandifolia)*

Distribution of grasses using C₄ mechanism in North America

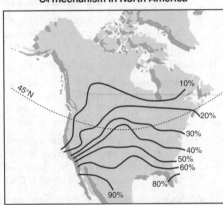

45°N

10%
20%
30%
40%
50%
60%
80%
90%

The photosynthetic strategy that a plant possesses is an important factor in determining where it lives. Because many of the enzymes of C₄ plants have optimum temperatures well above 25°C, they thrive in hot tropical and sub-tropical climates. Under these conditions, they can out-compete most C₃ plants because they achieve faster rates of photosynthesis. The proportion of grasses using the C₄ mechanism in North America is greatest near the tropics and diminishes northwards.

1. Explain why C₄ plants have a competitive advantage over C₃ plants in the tropics: _____

_____

_____

2. Explain why the bundle sheath cells are arranged in a way that keeps them isolated from air spaces in the leaf:

_____

_____

3. Study the map of North America above showing the distribution of C₄ plants. Explain the distribution pattern in terms of their competitive advantage and the environmental conditions required for this advantage:

_____

_____

_____

4. In C₃ plants, the rate of photosynthesis is enhanced by higher atmospheric CO₂ concentrations. Explain why this is not the case for C₄ plants:

_____

_____

Cellular Energetics

Code: A 2

Processes in the Nucleus

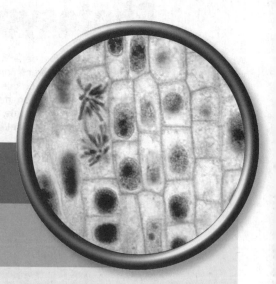

Investigating processes in the nucleus

The role of DNA in cells, for example in DNA replication and cell division. The genetic code and differentiation of cells.

Learning Objectives

☐ 1. Compile your own glossary from the **KEY WORDS** displayed in **bold type** in the learning objectives below.

The Cell Nucleus *(pages 89-91, 99)*

☐ 2. Recall the structure and role of the nucleus. Describe the nature of **nucleic acids** and the arrangement of nucleotides in **DNA**. Describe the basic structure and function of chromosomes and **genes**.

☐ 3. Describe the **semi-conservative replication** of DNA and its role in preparing the cell for division. Understand the base-pairing rule for creating a **complementary strand** from a **template strand** of DNA.

☐ 4. Explain the features of the **genetic code**, including:
   • The 4-letter alphabet and the 3-letter **triplet code** (**codon**) of base sequences.
   • The **non-overlapping**, linear nature of the code, which is read from a start point to a finish point.
   • Specific punctuation codons and their significance.
   • The **universal nature** and **degeneracy** of the code.

Mitosis and the Cell Cycle *(page 93)*

☐ 5. Describe the behaviour of **chromosomes** during the **cell cycle** in eukaryotes. Include: **mitosis**, **growth** (G_1 and G_2), and DNA replication (S).

☐ 6. Recognise and describe the following events in mitosis: **prophase**, **metaphase**, **anaphase**, and **telophase**. Recognise each of these stages in electron or light micrographs.

☐ 7. Describe **cytokinesis** in plant and animal cells, distinguishing between nuclear division and division of the cytoplasm.

☐ 8. Identify where mitosis occurs in plants and in animals. Understand the role of mitosis in growth and repair, and asexual reproduction. Recognise the importance of **daughter nuclei** with chromosomes identical in number and type. Recognise cell division as a prelude to **cellular differentiation**.

Cellular Differentiation *(pages 94-96)*

☐ 9. The root tip provides a good example of cellular differentiation. Distinguish between the structure and activity of different regions of a root tip: root cap, **meristem**, **zone of elongation**, **zone of differentiation**.

☐ 10. Demonstrate appropriate staining techniques in the study of mitosis in plant material, e.g. root tip squash.

☐ 11. Identify and describe the structural adaptations, role, and location of some specialised cells in humans, e.g. blood cells, liver cells, or intestinal epithelial cells.

The Role of Meiosis *(pages 92, 97-98)*

☐ 12. Contrast the final products of **mitosis** and **meiosis**. Explain what is meant by **homologous pairs** (of chromosomes), **haploid**, and **diploid**. Explain why a **reduction division** is necessary before fertilisation in sexual reproduction.

☐ 13. Distinguish between **meiosis I** and **meiosis II**, identifying the main features of these stages.

☐ 14. Identify the role of **crossing over** and **independent assortment** in meiosis, and state when these occur. Explain why the products of meiosis are haploid cells containing a single set of chromosomes. Explain how **fertilisation** restores the diploid number.

☐ 15. Describe how meiosis and fertilisation contribute to variation. Identify when and where meiosis might be carried out by a cell.

Supplementary Texts

See page 7 for additional details of these texts:

■ Adds, J., *et al.*, 2003. **Molecules and Cells**, (NelsonThornes), chpt. 4 as required.

■ Adds, J., E. Larkcom, R. Miller, & R. Sutton, 1999. **Tools, Techniques and Assessment in Biology**, (NelsonThornes), as required.

■ Harwood, R., 2002. **Biochemistry**, (Cambridge University Press), as required.

■ Tobin, A.J. and Morel, R.E., 1997. **Asking About Cells**, (Thomson Brooks/Cole), as required.

Periodicals

See page 7 for details of publishers of periodicals:

STUDENT'S REFERENCE

■ **The Cell Cycle and Mitosis** Biol. Sci. Rev., 14(4) April 2002, pp. 37-41. *Cell growth and division, key stages in the cell cycle, and the complex control over different stages of mitosis.*

■ **To Divide or Not to Divide** Biol. Sci. Rev., 11(4) March 1999, pp. 2-5. *The cell cycle: cell growth and stages of cell division and their control.*

■ **Mechanisms of Meiosis** Biol. Sci. Rev., 15(4), April 2003, pp. 20-24. *A clear and thorough account of the events and mechanisms of meiosis.*

Internet

See pages 4-5 for details of how to access topics via **Bio Links** from: **www.thebiozone.com**
CELL BIOLOGY AND BIOCHEMISTRY: • Cell & molecular biology online ... *and others*

GENETICS > Molecular Genetics (DNA): • Beginners guide to molecular biology • Center for Biomolecular Modeling • DNA interactive • DNA and molecular genetics ... *and others*

Presentation MEDIA to support this topic:

CELL BIO & BIOCHEM
Processes in the Nucleus

Cell Biology & Biochemistry

DNA Molecules

Even the smallest DNA molecules are extremely long. The DNA from the small *Polyoma* virus, for example, is 1.7 μm long; about three times longer than the longest proteins. The DNA comprising a bacterial chromosome is 1000 times longer than the cell into which it has to fit. The amount of DNA present in the nucleus of the cells of eukaryotic organisms varies widely from one species to another. In vertebrate sex cells, the quantity of DNA ranges from 40 000 **kb** to 80 000 000 **kb**, with humans about in the middle of the range. The traditional focus of DNA research has been on those DNA sequences that code for proteins, yet protein-coding DNA accounts for less than 2% of the DNA in human chromosomes. The rest of the DNA, once dismissed as non-coding 'evolutionary junk', is now recognised as giving rise to functional RNA molecules, many of which have already been identified as having important regulatory functions. While there is no clear correspondence between the complexity of an organism and the number of protein-coding genes in its genome, this is not the case for non-protein-coding DNA. The genomes of more complex organisms contain much more of this so-called "non-coding" DNA. These RNA-only 'hidden' genes tend to be short and difficult to identify, but the sequences are highly conserved and clearly have a role in inheritance, development, and health.

Sizes of DNA Molecules			
Group	Organism	Base pairs (in 1000s, or kb)	Length
Viruses	Polyoma or SV40	5.1	1.7 μm
	Lambda phage	48.6	17 μm
	T2 phage	166	56 μm
	Vaccinia	190	65 μm
Bacteria	Mycoplasma	760	260 μm
	E. coli (from human gut)	4600	1.56 mm
Eukaryotes	Yeast	13 500	4.6 mm
	Drosophila (fruit fly)	165 000	5.6 cm
	Human	2 900 000	99 cm

Kilobase (kb)

A kilobase is unit of length equal to 1000 base pairs of a double-stranded nucleic acid molecule (or 1000 bases of a single-stranded molecule). One kb of double stranded DNA has a length of 0.34 μm. (1 μm = 1/1000 mm)

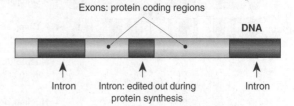

Exons: protein coding regions

DNA

Intron   Intron: edited out during protein synthesis   Intron

Most protein-coding genes in eukaryotic DNA are not continuous and may be interrupted by 'intrusions' of other pieces of DNA. Protein-coding regions (**exons**) are interrupted by non-protein-coding regions called **introns**. Introns range in frequency from 1 to over 30 in a single 'gene' and also in size (100 to more than 10 000 bases). Introns are edited out of the protein-coding sequence during protein synthesis, but probably, after processing, go on to serve a regulatory function.

Giant lampbrush chromosomes

Lampbrush chromosomes are large chromosomes found in amphibian eggs, with lateral loops of DNA that produce a brushlike appearance under the microscope. The two scanning electron micrographs (below and right) show minute strands of DNA giving a fuzzy appearance in the high power view.

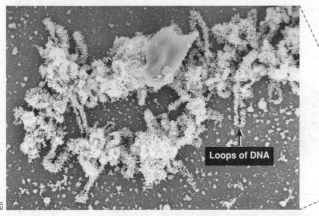

Loops of DNA

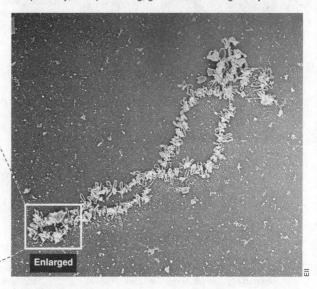

Enlarged

Processes in the Nucleus

1. Consult the table above and make the following comparisons. Determine how much more DNA is present in:

   (a) The bacterium *E. coli* compared to the Lambda Phage virus: _____

   (b) Human cells compared to the bacteria *E. coli:* _____

2. State what proportion of DNA in a eukaryotic cell is used to code for proteins or structural RNA: _____

3. Describe two reasons why geneticists have reevaluated their traditional view that one gene codes for one polypeptide:

   (a) _____

   _____

   (b) _____

   _____

The Role of DNA in Cells

A cell's total genetic endowment of DNA is called its **genome**. Arranged along the length of each DNA molecule are hundreds of genes: the hereditary units that specify an organism's characteristics. Every cell in the body of an organism contains **all** the genes for **all** the body's metabolism. When cells take on a specific role, such as that of a skin cell, only the information required for that cell's function is carried out. Other genes are turned off. The genetic instructions from the nucleus are carried to the cytoplasm where they are used to create proteins by protein synthesis. In eukaryotes, the DNA is coiled and folded into **chromosomes**. Chromosomes are visible with a light microscope just before and during cell division. Every species has a characteristic number of chromosomes in each nucleus (e.g. humans have 46 chromosomes in somatic cells). Reproductive cells (gametes) have half as many chromosomes as somatic cells (23 in humans).

The Structure and Role of the Nucleus

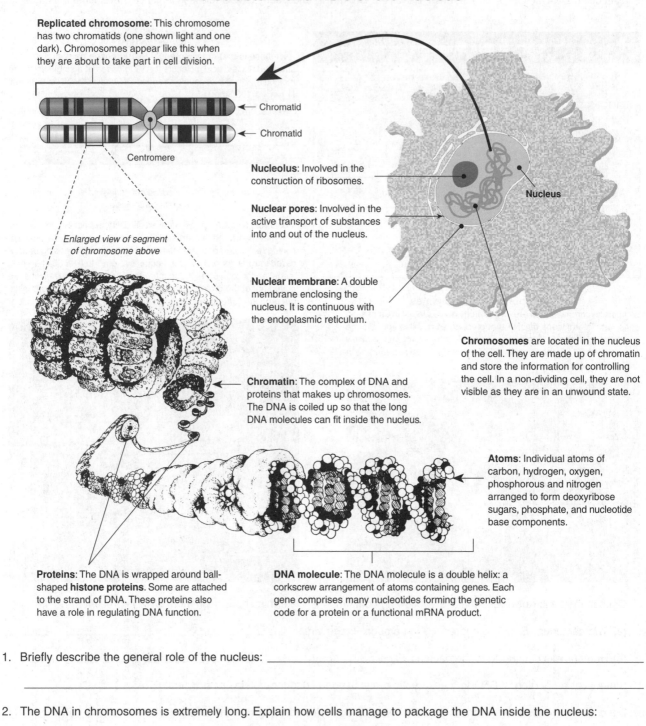

Replicated chromosome: This chromosome has two chromatids (one shown light and one dark). Chromosomes appear like this when they are about to take part in cell division.

← Chromatid

← Chromatid

Centromere

Enlarged view of segment of chromosome above

Nucleolus: Involved in the construction of ribosomes.

Nuclear pores: Involved in the active transport of substances into and out of the nucleus.

Nuclear membrane: A double membrane enclosing the nucleus. It is continuous with the endoplasmic reticulum.

Nucleus

Chromosomes are located in the nucleus of the cell. They are made up of chromatin and store the information for controlling the cell. In a non-dividing cell, they are not visible as they are in an unwound state.

Chromatin: The complex of DNA and proteins that makes up chromosomes. The DNA is coiled up so that the long DNA molecules can fit inside the nucleus.

Atoms: Individual atoms of carbon, hydrogen, oxygen, phosphorous and nitrogen arranged to form deoxyribose sugars, phosphate, and nucleotide base components.

Proteins: The DNA is wrapped around ball-shaped **histone proteins**. Some are attached to the strand of DNA. These proteins also have a role in regulating DNA function.

DNA molecule: The DNA molecule is a double helix: a corkscrew arrangement of atoms containing genes. Each gene comprises many nucleotides forming the genetic code for a protein or a functional mRNA product.

1. Briefly describe the general role of the nucleus: _____

_____

2. The DNA in chromosomes is extremely long. Explain how cells manage to package the DNA inside the nucleus:

_____

_____

3. State when in the cell cycle a chromosome consists of a:

   (a) Single chromatid: _____   (b) Two chromatids: _____

DNA Replication

Cells carry out the process of **DNA replication** (DNA duplication) prior to cell division (mitosis and meiosis). This process ensures that each resulting cell is able to receive a complete set of genes from the original cell. Upon completion of DNA replication, each chromosome is made up of two chromatids which are joined at the centromere. Each chromatid contains half original (parent) DNA and half new (daughter) DNA. The two chromatids will become separated during cell division to form two separate chromosomes. During DNA replication, new nucleotides become added at a region called the **replication fork**. The position of the replication fork moves along the chromosome as the replication progresses. This whole process occurs simultaneously for each chromosome of a cell and the entire process is tightly controlled by enzymes.

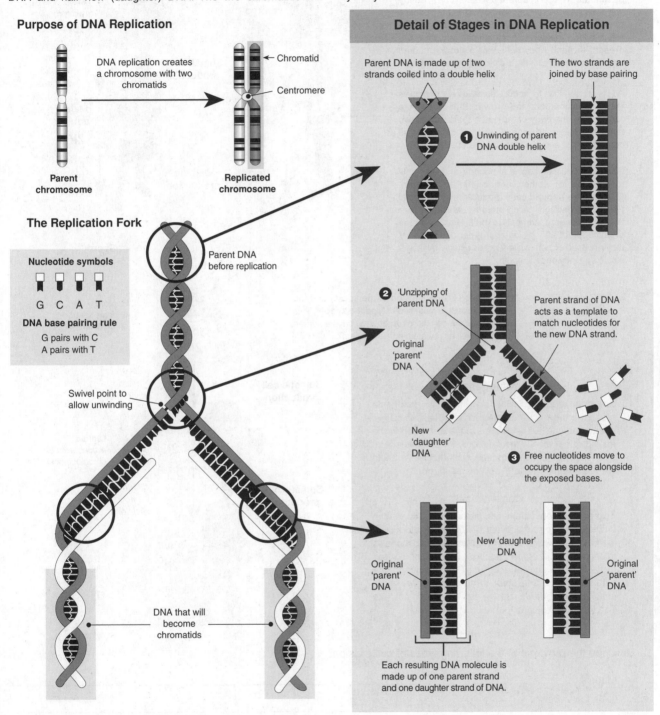

Purpose of DNA Replication

DNA replication creates a chromosome with two chromatids

Parent chromosome → Replicated chromosome — Chromatid, Centromere

The Replication Fork

Nucleotide symbols

G   C   A   T

DNA base pairing rule
G pairs with C
A pairs with T

Parent DNA before replication

Swivel point to allow unwinding

DNA that will become chromatids

Detail of Stages in DNA Replication

Parent DNA is made up of two strands coiled into a double helix

The two strands are joined by base pairing

1 Unwinding of parent DNA double helix

2 'Unzipping' of parent DNA

Original 'parent' DNA

New 'daughter' DNA

Parent strand of DNA acts as a template to match nucleotides for the new DNA strand.

3 Free nucleotides move to occupy the space alongside the exposed bases.

New 'daughter' DNA

Original 'parent' DNA

Original 'parent' DNA

Each resulting DNA molecule is made up of one parent strand and one daughter strand of DNA.

Processes in the Nucleus

1. State the purpose of DNA replication: _____

2. Summarise the three main steps involved in DNA replication:

    (a) _____

    (b) _____

    (c) _____

3. For a cell with 22 chromosomes, state how many chromatids would exist following DNA replication: _____

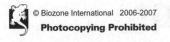

Code: A 2

Cell Division

The life cycle of **diploid sexually reproducing organisms** (such as humans) is illustrated in the diagram below. **Gametogenesis** is the process responsible for the production of male and female gametes for the purpose of sexual reproduction. The difference between meiosis in males and in females should be noted (see spermatogenesis and oogenesis in the box below).

Human embryos have cells which are rapidly dividing by **mitosis**. The term **somatic** means 'body', so the cell divisions are creating new body cells (as opposed to gametes or sex cells). The **2N** or **diploid** number refers to how many whole sets of chromosomes are present in each body cell. For a normal human embryo, all cells will have a diploid number of 46.

Adults still continue to produce somatic cells by mitosis for cell replacement and growth. Blood cells are replaced by the body at the astonishing rate of two million per second, and a layer of skin cells is constantly lost and replaced about every 28 days.

Gamete production begins at puberty, and lasts until menopause for women, and indefinitely for men. Gametes are **haploid cells** produced by the special type of cell division, called **meiosis**, which reduces the chromosome number to half. Human males produce about 200 million sperm per day (whether they are used or not), while females usually release a single egg only once a month.

Fertilisation involves fusion of the sperm and the egg to produce a single cell called the **zygote**. This cell has all the genetic information to build a human body as well as maintain it (metabolism).

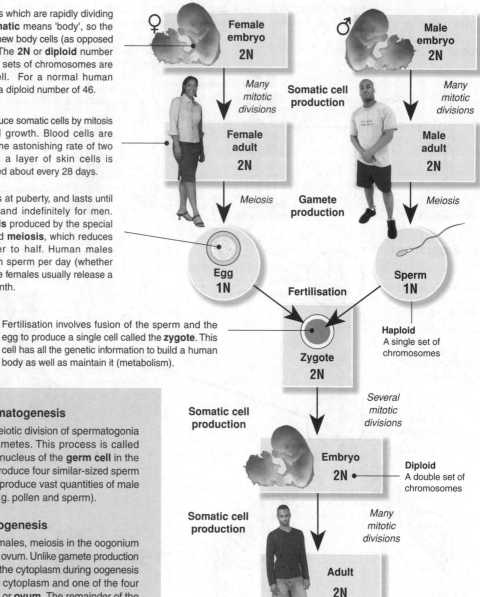

Spermatogenesis

Sperm production: Meiotic division of spermatogonia produces the male gametes. This process is called spermatogenesis. The nucleus of the **germ cell** in the male divides twice to produce four similar-sized sperm cells. Many organisms produce vast quantities of male gametes in this way (e.g. pollen and sperm).

Oogenesis

Egg production: In females, meiosis in the oogonium produces the egg cell or ovum. Unlike gamete production in males, the divison of the cytoplasm during oogenesis is unequal. Most of the cytoplasm and one of the four nuclei form the egg cell or **ovum**. The remainder of the cytoplasm, plus the other three nuclei, form much smaller **polar bodies** and are abortive (i.e. do not take part in fertilisation and formation of the zygote).

1. Describe the **purpose** of the following types of cell division:

   (a) Mitosis: _____

   _____

   (b) Meiosis: _____

   _____

2. Explain the significance of the **zygote**: _____

3. Describe the basic difference between the cell divisions involved in spermatogenesis and oogenesis:

   _____

   _____

Mitosis and the Cell Cycle

Mitosis is part of the 'cell cycle' in which an existing cell (the parent cell) divides into two new ones (the daughter cells). Mitosis does not result in a change of chromosome numbers (unlike meiosis): the daughter cells are identical to the parent cell. Although mitosis is part of a continuous cell cycle, it is divided into stages (below). In plants and animals mitosis is associated with growth and repair of tissue, and it is the method by which some organisms reproduce asexually. The example below illustrates the cell cycle in a plant cell. Note that in animal cells, **cytokinesis** involves the formation of a constriction that divides the cell in two. It is usually well underway by the end of telophase and does not involve the formation of a cell plate.

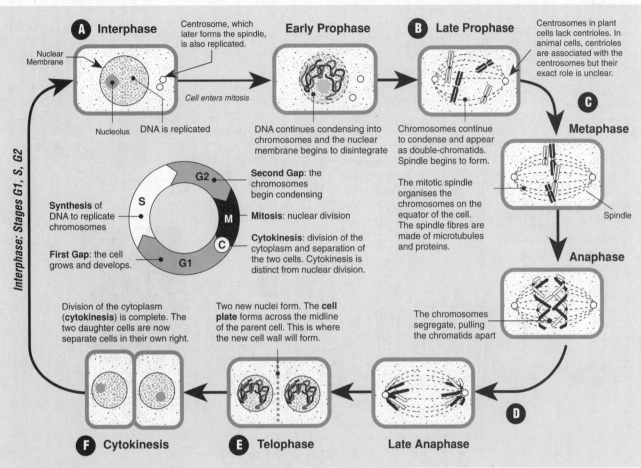

Interphase: Stages G1, S, G2

A Interphase
Nuclear Membrane
Centrosome, which later forms the spindle, is also replicated.
Nucleolus   DNA is replicated
Cell enters mitosis

Early Prophase
DNA continues condensing into chromosomes and the nuclear membrane begins to disintegrate

B Late Prophase
Chromosomes continue to condense and appear as double-chromatids. Spindle begins to form.

Centrosomes in plant cells lack centrioles. In animal cells, centrioles are associated with the centrosomes but their exact role is unclear.

C Metaphase
The mitotic spindle organises the chromosomes on the equator of the cell. The spindle fibres are made of microtubules and proteins.
Spindle

Anaphase
The chromosomes segregate, pulling the chromatids apart

G2 **Second Gap**: the chromosomes begin condensing
Synthesis of DNA to replicate chromosomes
S
M **Mitosis**: nuclear division
C **Cytokinesis**: division of the cytoplasm and separation of the two cells. Cytokinesis is distinct from nuclear division.
First Gap: the cell grows and develops.
G1

Division of the cytoplasm (**cytokinesis**) is complete. The two daughter cells are now separate cells in their own right.

Two new nuclei form. The **cell plate** forms across the midline of the parent cell. This is where the new cell wall will form.

F Cytokinesis   **E Telophase**   **Late Anaphase**   **D**

1. The five photographs below were taken at various stages through the process of mitosis in a plant cell. They are not in any particular order. Study the diagram above and determine the stage that each photograph represents (e.g. anaphase).

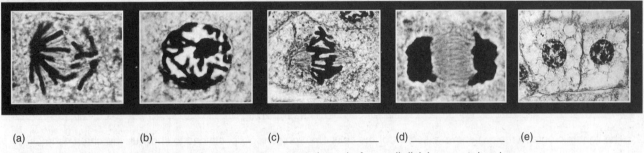

Photos: RCN

(a) _____   (b) _____   (c) _____   (d) _____   (e) _____

2. State two important changes that chromosomes must undergo before cell division can take place:

_____

3. Briefly summarise the stages of the cell cycle by describing what is happening at the points (**A-F**) in the diagram above:

A. _____

B. _____

C. _____

D. _____

E. _____

F. _____

Processes in the Nucleus

Code: A 1

Root Cell Development

In plants, cell division for growth (mitosis) is restricted to growing tips called **meristematic** tissue. These are located at the tips of every stem and root. This is unlike mitosis in a growing animal where cell divisions can occur all over the body. The diagram below illustrates the position and appearance of developing and growing cells in a plant root. Similar zones of development occur in the growing stem tips, which may give rise to specialised structures such as leaves and flowers.

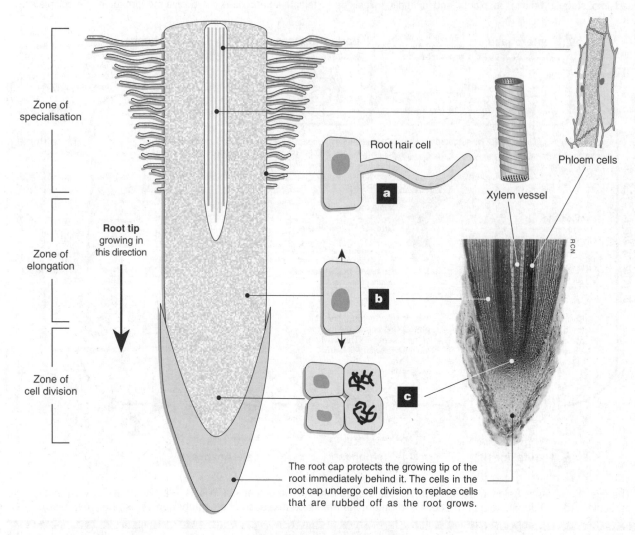

Zone of specialisation

Root hair cell

a

Xylem vessel

Phloem cells

Root tip
growing in this direction

Zone of elongation

b

Zone of cell division

c

The root cap protects the growing tip of the root immediately behind it. The cells in the root cap undergo cell division to replace cells that are rubbed off as the root grows.

1. Briefly describe what is happening to the plant cells at each of the points labelled (**a**) to (**c**) in the diagram above:

   (a) _____

   (b) _____

   (c) _____

2. The light micrograph (below) shows a section of the cells of an onion root tip, stained to show up the chromosomes.

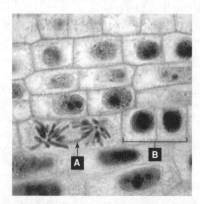

A   B

   (a) State the mitotic stage of the cell labelled A and explain your answer:

   _____

   (b) State the mitotic stage just completed in the cells labelled B and explain:

   _____

   (c) If, in this example, 250 cells were examined and 25 were found to be in the process of mitosis, state the proportion of the cell cycle occupied by mitosis:

   _____

   _____

3. Identify the cells that divide and specialise when a tree increases its girth (diameter): _____

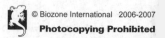

Differentiation of Human Cells

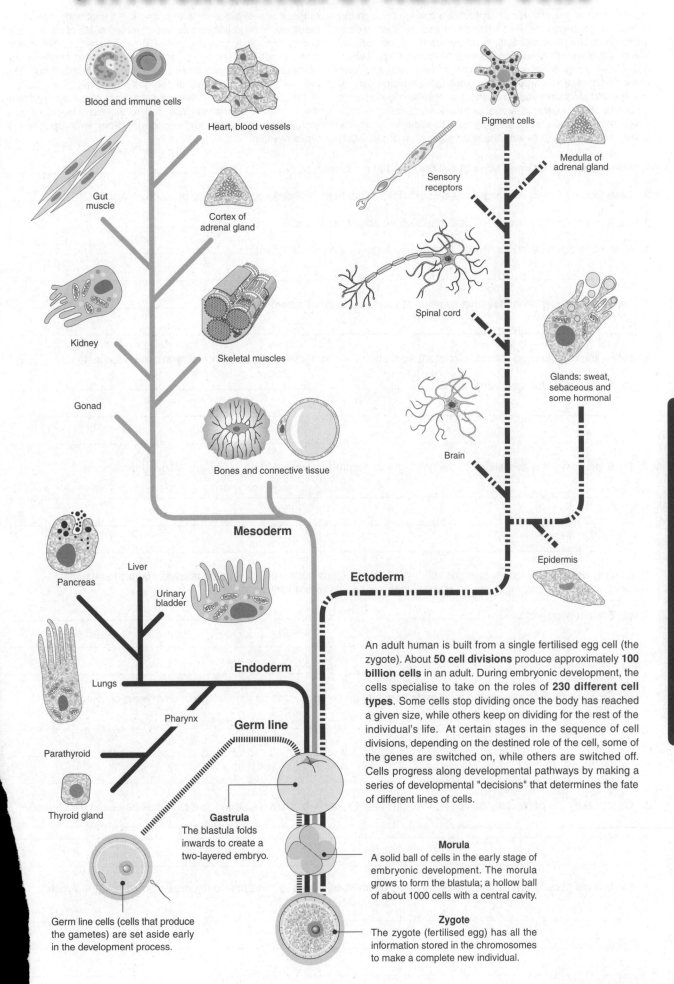

Blood and immune cells

Heart, blood vessels

Pigment cells

Medulla of adrenal gland

Gut muscle

Cortex of adrenal gland

Sensory receptors

Kidney

Skeletal muscles

Spinal cord

Glands: sweat, sebaceous and some hormonal

Gonad

Bones and connective tissue

Brain

Mesoderm

Epidermis

Ectoderm

Pancreas

Liver

Urinary bladder

Endoderm

Lungs

Pharynx

Germ line

Parathyroid

Thyroid gland

An adult human is built from a single fertilised egg cell (the zygote). About **50 cell divisions** produce approximately **100 billion cells** in an adult. During embryonic development, the cells specialise to take on the roles of **230 different cell types**. Some cells stop dividing once the body has reached a given size, while others keep on dividing for the rest of the individual's life. At certain stages in the sequence of cell divisions, depending on the destined role of the cell, some of the genes are switched on, while others are switched off. Cells progress along developmental pathways by making a series of developmental "decisions" that determines the fate of different lines of cells.

Gastrula
The blastula folds inwards to create a two-layered embryo.

Morula
A solid ball of cells in the early stage of embryonic development. The morula grows to form the blastula; a hollow ball of about 1000 cells with a central cavity.

Zygote
The zygote (fertilised egg) has all the information stored in the chromosomes to make a complete new individual.

Germ line cells (cells that produce the gametes) are set aside early in the development process.

Processes in the Nucleus

Code: RA 2

Development is the process of progressive change through the lifetime of an organism. Part of this process involves growth (increase in size) and cell division (to generate the multicellular body). Cellular **differentiation** (the generation of specialised cells) and morphogenesis (the creation of the shape and form of the body) are also part of development. Differentiation defines the specific structure and function of a cell. As development proceeds, the possibilities available to individual cells become fewer, until each cell's **fate** is determined. The tissues and organs making up the body form from the aggregation and organisation of these differentiated cells. In animals, the final body form is the result of cell migration and the programmed death of certain cells during embryonic development. The diagram opposite shows how a single fertilised egg (zygote) gives rise to the large number of specialised cell types that make up the adult human body. The morula, blastula, and gastrula stages mentioned at the bottom of the diagram show the early development of the embryo from the zygote. The gastrula gives rise to the three layers of cells (ectoderm, mesoderm, and endoderm), from which specific cell types develop.

1. State how many different types of cell are found in the human body: _____

2. State approximately how many cell divisions take place from fertilised egg (zygote) to produce an adult: _____

3. State approximately how many cells make up an adult human body: _____

4. Name one cell type that continues to divide throughout a person's lifetime: _____

   _____

5. Name one cell type that does not continue to divide throughout a person's lifetime: _____

   _____

6. Germ line cells diverge (become isolated) from other cells at a very early stage in embryonic development.

   (a) Explain what the **germ line** is: _____

   _____

   _____

   (b) Explain why it is necessary for the germ line to become separated at such an early stage of development:

   _____

   _____

   _____

7. Cloning whole new organisms is possible by taking a nucleus from a cell during the blastula stage of embryonic development and placing it into an egg cell that has had its own nucleus removed.

   (a) Explain what a **clone** is: _____

   _____

   _____

   (b) Explain why the cell required for cloning needs to be taken at such an early stage of embryonic development:

   _____

   _____

   _____

8. Cancer cells are particularly damaging to organisms. Explain what has happened to a cell that has become cancerous:

   _____

   _____

9. Explain the genetic events that enable so many different cell types to arise from one unspecialised cell (the zygote):

   _____

   _____

   _____

Meiosis

Meiosis is a special type of cell division concerned with producing sex cells (gametes) for the purpose of sexual reproduction. It involves a single chromosomal duplication followed by two successive nuclear divisions, and results in a halving of the diploid chromosome number. Meiosis occurs in the sex organs of plants and animals. If genetic mistakes (**gene** and **chromosome mutations**) occur here, they will be inherited. A comparison of mitosis and meiosis is shown on the following page.

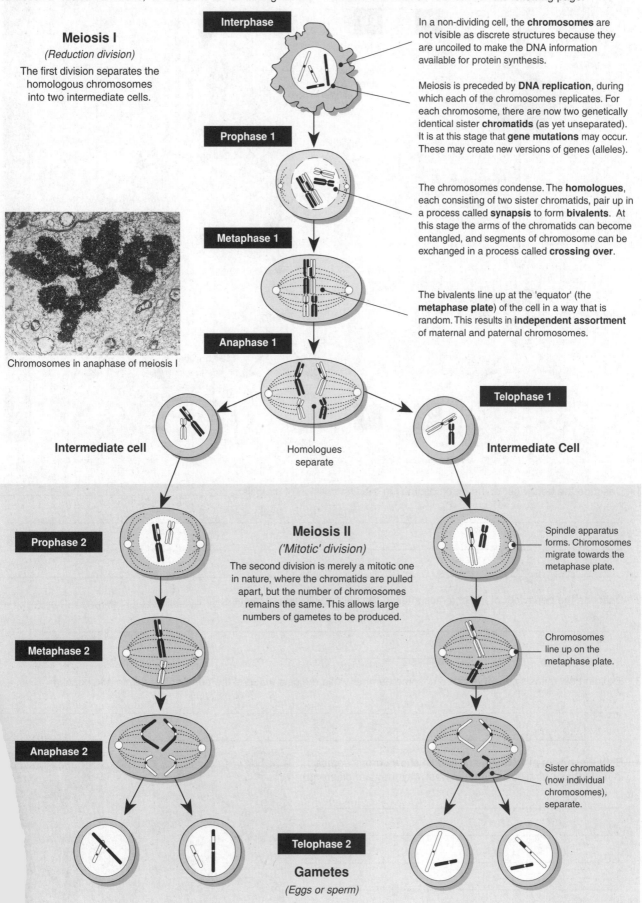

Chromosomes in anaphase of meiosis I

Meiosis I
(Reduction division)

The first division separates the homologous chromosomes into two intermediate cells.

Interphase

In a non-dividing cell, the **chromosomes** are not visible as discrete structures because they are uncoiled to make the DNA information available for protein synthesis.

Meiosis is preceded by **DNA replication**, during which each of the chromosomes replicates. For each chromosome, there are now two genetically identical sister **chromatids** (as yet unseparated). It is at this stage that **gene mutations** may occur. These may create new versions of genes (alleles).

Prophase 1

The chromosomes condense. The **homologues**, each consisting of two sister chromatids, pair up in a process called **synapsis** to form **bivalents**. At this stage the arms of the chromatids can become entangled, and segments of chromosome can be exchanged in a process called **crossing over**.

Metaphase 1

The bivalents line up at the 'equator' (the **metaphase plate**) of the cell in a way that is random. This results in **independent assortment** of maternal and paternal chromosomes.

Anaphase 1

Telophase 1

Intermediate cell

Homologues separate

Intermediate Cell

Meiosis II
('Mitotic' division)

The second division is merely a mitotic one in nature, where the chromatids are pulled apart, but the number of chromosomes remains the same. This allows large numbers of gametes to be produced.

Prophase 2

Metaphase 2

Anaphase 2

Telophase 2

Gametes
(Eggs or sperm)

Spindle apparatus forms. Chromosomes migrate towards the metaphase plate.

Chromosomes line up on the metaphase plate.

Sister chromatids (now individual chromosomes), separate.

Processes in the Nucleus

Code: RA 1

Mitosis

Meiosis

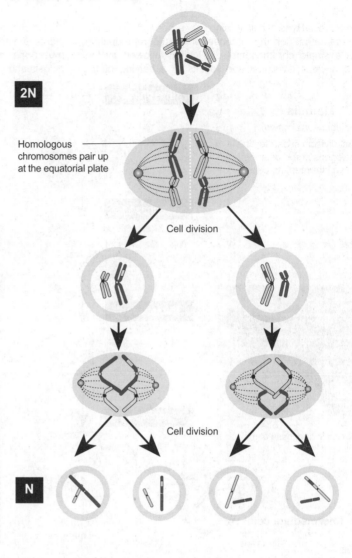

2N

2N

Homologous chromosomes pair up at the equatorial plate

Cell division

Homologous chromosomes **do not** pair up at the equatorial plate

Cell division

Cell division

2N

N

Meiosis I: Reduction division

Meiosis II: 'Mitotic' division

1. Describe the behaviour of the chromosomes in the first division of meiosis: _____

_____

_____

_____

2. Describe the behaviour of the chromosomes in the second division of meiosis: _____

_____

_____

3. Explain how mitosis conserves chromosome number while meiosis reduces the number from diploid to haploid:

_____

_____

4. Both these light micrographs (**A** and **B**) show chromosomes in metaphase of meiosis. State in what way they are different:

_____

_____

_____

_____

_____

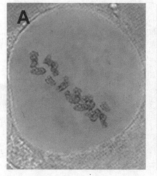

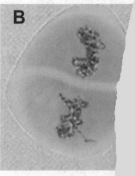

A

B

The Genetic Code

The genetic information that codes for the assembly of amino acids is stored as three-letter codes, called **codons**. Each codon represents one of 20 amino acids used in the construction of polypeptide chains. The **mRNA-amino acid table** (bottom of page) can be used to identify the amino acid encoded by each of the mRNA codons. Note that the code is **degenerate** in that for each amino acid, there may be more than one codon. Most of this degeneracy involves the third nucleotide of a codon. The genetic code is **universal**; all living organisms on Earth, from viruses and bacteria, to plants and humans, share the same genetic code (with a few minor exceptions representing mutations that have occurred over the long history of evolution).

Amino acid		Codons that code for this amino acid	No.	Amino acid		Codons that code for this amino acid	No.
Ala	Alanine	GCU, GCC, GCA, GCG	4	**Leu**	Leucine		
Arg	Arginine			**Lys**	Lysine		
Asn	Asparagine			**Met**	Methionine		
Asp	Aspartic acid			**Phe**	Phenylalanine		
Cys	Cysteine			**Pro**	Proline		
Gln	Glutamine			**Ser**	Serine		
Glu	Glutamic acid			**Thr**	Threonine		
Gly	Glycine			**Try**	Tryptophan		
His	Histidine			**Tyr**	Tyrosine		
Iso	Isoleucine			**Val**	Valine		

1. Use the **mRNA-amino acid table** (below) to list in the table above all the **codons** that code for each of the amino acids and the number of different codons that can code for each amino acid (the first amino acid has been done for you).

2. (a) State how many amino acids could be coded for if a codon consisted of just two bases: _____

   (b) Explain why this number of bases is inadequate to code for the 20 amino acids required to make proteins:

   _____

   _____

3. Describe the consequence of the degeneracy of the genetic code to the likely effect of a change to one base in a triplet:

   _____

   _____

mRNA-Amino Acid Table

How to read the table: The table on the right is used to 'decode' the genetic code as ¦ sequence of amino acids in a polypeptide ¦ain, from a given mRNA sequence. To ¦rk out which amino acid is coded for by a ¦don (triplet of bases) look for the first letter ¦he codon in the row label on the left hand ¦. Then look for the column that intersects ¦same row from above that matches the ¦nd base. Finally, locate the third base in ¦odon by looking along the row from the ¦hand end that matches your codon.

¦ple: Determine **CAG**

¦on the left row, A on the top column,
¦on the right row
¦**AG** is Gln (**glutamine**)

Read second letter here

Read first letter here

Read third letter here

		Second Letter				
First Letter		U	C	A	G	Third Letter
U		UUU Phe UUC Phe UUA Leu UUG Leu	UCU Ser UCC Ser UCA Ser UCG Ser	UAU Tyr UAC Tyr UAA STOP UAG STOP	UGU Cys UGC Cys UGA STOP UGG Try	U C A G
C		CUU Leu CUC Leu CUA Leu CUG Leu	CCU Pro CCC Pro CCA Pro CCG Pro	CAU His CAC His CAA Gln CAG Gln	CGU Arg CGC Arg CGA Arg CGG Arg	U C A G
A		AUU Iso AUC Iso AUA Iso AUG Met	ACU Thr ACC Thr ACA Thr ACG Thr	AAU Asn AAC Asn AAA Lys AAG Lys	AGU Ser AGC Ser AGA Arg AGG Arg	U C A G
G		GUU Val GUC Val GUA Val GUG Val	GCU Ala GCC Ala GCA Ala GCG Ala	GAU Asp GAC Asp GAA Glu GAG Glu	GGU Gly GGC Gly GGA Gly GGG Gly	U C A G

Processes in the Nucleus

Code: A 2

Index